Electronics for
Technicians 2

Electronics
for Technicians 2

S. A. Knight BSc(Hons)Lond

Senior Lecturer in Mathematics & Electronic Engineering, Bedford
College of Higher Education

THE BUTTERWORTH GROUP

UNITED KINGDOM	Butterworth & Co. (Publishers) Ltd London: 88 Kingsway, WC2B 6AB
AUSTRALIA	Butterworths Pty Ltd Sydney: 586 Pacific Highway, Chatswood, NSW 2067 Also at Melbourne, Brisbane, Adelaide and Perth
CANADA	Butterworth & Co. (Canada) Ltd Toronto: 2265 Midland Avenue, Scarborough, Ontario M1P 4S1
NEW ZEALAND	Butterworths of New Zealand Ltd Wellington: T & W Young Building, 77–85 Customhouse Quay, 1, CPO Box 472
SOUTH AFRICA	Butterworth & Co. (South Africa) (Pty) Ltd Durban: 152–154 Gale Street
USA	Butterworth (Publishers) Inc Boston: 19 Cummings Park, Woburn, Mass. 01801

First published 1978

© S. A. Knight, 1978

British Library Cataloguing in Publication Data

Knight, Stephen Alfred
    Electronics for technicians 2. – (Technician series).
    1. Electronic apparatus and appliances
    I. Title   II. Series
    621.381   TK7870   77–30752

    ISBN 0–408–00324–3

Typeset and produced by Scribe Design, Chatham, Kent
Printed in England by Page Bros Ltd., Norwich, Norfolk

Preface

This book covers the essential syllabus requirements of TEC Unit U76/010 for Electronics 2. Although the TEC guide syllabus has been followed to a large extent, there are occasionally some additional notes on particular topics where their inclusion seemed justified for the sake of clarity.

The basic theory and application of semiconductors is a difficult subject to put over in an elementary manner. In setting it out in this present form some technical licence has been taken on a few occasions and only the absolute essentials of the subject receive attention. In this way the flow of reasoning is less likely to be side-tracked by the introduction of topics not immediately required for the programme. Much of such subsidiary information can be safely left to the class lecturer where it rightly belongs.

The book is intended to be used in the order written. Each section should be carefully read in conjunction with the illustrations, the worked examples followed through where they turn up, the assignment problems attempted and checked against the solutions before the following section is approached. In this way the course will proceed in a series of logical steps and at no point will a new or unfamiliar concept appear that has not already been explained or is not in the process of being explained.

Nearly all test problems have been designed strictly to illustrate the foregoing text and to avoid the introduction of clumsy numbers into the necessary calculations. Method is the requirement, and method is more readily acquired without the distraction of number-juggling. Some of the solutions contain additional information and such notes should be treated as part of the main text.

I would be grateful to have any errors which may have slipped through the most careful scrutiny pointed out to me, and other constructive comments would be most welcome.

S.A.K.

Contents

1 THERMIONIC AND
   SEMICONDUCTOR THEORY

Structure of atoms 1
Conduction 3
Thermionic Emission 3
Cathodes 4
Semiconductors 5
Impurity atoms 7
Problems for Section 1 8

2 SEMICONDUCTOR AND
   THERMIONIC DIODES

The junction diode 11
The thermionic diode 14
Comparisons 15
Problems for Section 2 16

3 APPLICATIONS OF
   SEMICONDUCTOR DIODES

Rectifier circuits 18
The half-wave rectifier 19
The full-wave rectifier 20
The bridge rectifier 21
Practical diode ratings 21
Smoothing circuits 23
The Zener diode 24
The Zener stabiliser 25
Zener protection 28
The varactor diode 29
Problems for Section 3 29

4 THE BIPOLAR TRANSISTOR

The junction transistor 31
Circuit configurations 33
Characteristic curves 35
Problems for Section 4 41

5 THE TRANSISTOR AS AMPLIFIER

The general amplifier 43
The common-emitter amplifier 44
Using the characteristic curves 47
Leakage current 51
Setting the operating point 52
Thermal runaway 55
Gain estimations 55
Problems for section 5 56

6 OSCILLATORS

Types of oscillator 60
The oscillatory tuned circuit 60
Oscillation frequency 61
The L-C oscillator 62
Common-emitter oscillators 63
Relaxation oscillators 65
Problems for Section 6 66

7 THE CATHODE RAY TUBE

The electron gun 67
The deflecting system 69
Deflection sensitivity 70
The screen 72
The timebase 72
Problems for Section 7 73

8 LOGIC CIRCUITS

Positive and negative logic 76
Rules of circuit logic 76
Negation 79
Logical relations 81
Testing for logical equivalence 82
Problems for Section 8 83

9 ELECTRONIC GATE ELEMENTS

Electronic gates 85
A fundamental diode gate 85
The diode AND gate 86
The diode OR gate 87
The NOT gate 89
Circuit representation of logical expressions 89
Problems for Section 9 92

SOLUTIONS TO PROBLEMS 94

APPENDIX 99

1 Thermionic and semiconductor theory

Aims: At the end of this Unit section you should be able to:
Understand the general structure of atoms.
Understand and describe the effects of thermionic emission.
Define the properties of conductors, insulators and semiconductors.
Name the majority charge carriers in p- *and* n-*type material.*
State the effect of temperature upon intrinsic conduction in semiconducting materials.

Electronics may be defined as *the study of the behaviour of electrons and the practical uses to which such study can be applied.* Up to about 25 years ago the term was associated almost exclusively with the theory and utilisation of thermionic valves, and all practical applications such as radio and television receivers, amplifiers, radar installations and control systems in industry depended upon the thermionic valve.

Over the intervening years the valve has been gradually replaced by the bipolar transistor, and this in turn is being replaced by field effect devices. Complicated circuits which, even with transistors, occupied a great amount of space are being replaced by integrated circuits which at the most occupy only a few cubic centimetres yet perform the work of hundreds of discrete transistors and their associated circuit components.

Although thermionic valves are now obsolete in many applications, they remain superior in a number of high frequency and high power domains, and they are, of course, still found in considerable numbers in equipments such as television receivers and industrial control systems. The cathode ray tube, the vital component of all television receivers and laboratory oscilloscopes, is a thermionic device. The principles involved are therefore worth some discussion, although the main emphasis will be upon semiconductors and associated devices. It is well to bear in mind that a grasp of the principles of thermionic valves is a very useful stepping stone to an understanding of semiconductors, particularly field effect devices where the analogous behaviour of valves and semiconductors is particularly well illustrated.

In this present Unit section we shall consequently introduce the basic theory not only of the semiconductor but also of the thermionic valve, to begin studying the operation and application of these electronic devices in general.

STRUCTURE OF ATOMS

All matter exists in a solid, liquid or gaseous state. Matter in any of these states is made up of very small particles known as *molecules*, which in turn are composed of *atoms*. Atoms can be envisaged as minute planetary systems, having a nucleus or core which carries a positive charge of electricity, around which revolve small charges of negative electricity known as *electrons*. The mass of an electron is estimated to be about 9.1×10^{-31} kilograms (kg) and the charge it carries is about -1.6×10^{-19} coulomb (C). Both of these quantities are unimaginably small, but it is upon the electron, nevertheless, that the whole science of electronics depends. Normally an atom is electrically neutral, the effect of the negative charges carried by the revolving electrons being exactly balanced by the overall positive charge carried by the nucleus. The nucleus is not just a solid lump; it is made up of two other types of particles, *protons* and *neutrons*. Only the protons carry positive charges, the neutrons being without charge. The charge on each proton, since it neutralises the charge on an electron, is the same as that of an electron but of opposite sign. The proton, however, is about 1840 times as massive as an electron, so that a quick calculation gives its mass as 1.67×10^{-27} kg. Do the calculation for yourself.

The revolving electrons are pictured as moving in elliptical orbits around the nucleus, held in their respective orbital rings, or *shells* as they are more usually called, by the attractive force of the nucleus. The different shells are distinguished by assigning to them letters of the alphabet, starting at K for the innermost, and proceeding through L, M, N, etc., to the outermost. The electrons (or electron) making up the outermost shell are called *valence electrons*, and these being farthest from the attractive force of the nucleus are least tightly bound in the complete atomic assemblage. It is the valence electrons that play the active part in electrical conduction.

Figure 1.1 shows atoms of hydrogen and helium, both very light gases; and *Figure 1.2* shows the atoms of *germanium* and *silicon*, two very important elements in the manufacture of transistors. You should notice that each of these last two atoms has four valence electrons.

Hydrogen atom – a single proton around which revolves a single electron

Helium atom – a nucleus of two protons and two neutrons with two orbital electrons

Figure 1.1

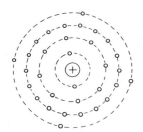

Germanium atom – a nucleus of 32 protons and 42 neutrons with 4 shells containing respectively 2, 8, 18 and 4 orbital electrons

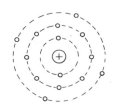

Silicon atom – a nucleus of 14 protons and 14 neutrons with 3 shells containing respectively 2, 8 and 4 orbital electrons

Figure 1.2

Bear in mind also that the diagrams are simply two-dimensional representations of the atoms and that in reality the orbiting electrons neither rotate in circles nor lie in one plane.

(1) The K, L, M and N shells of a copper atom contain, in order, 2, 8, 18 and 1 electron. How many protons are there in the nucleus?

(2) The atom of aluminium has a nucleus made up of 13 protons and 14 neutrons. In the two inner shells there are 2 and 8 electrons respectively. How many valence electrons are there in the aluminium atom?

CONDUCTION

In metals, and in the non-metallic element carbon, the valence electrons are easily displaced from their orbital shells, so that there is normally a great number of 'free' electrons wandering about within the material. These electrons haphazardly attach themselves to or detach themselves from atoms, or dance about in transit between the atoms. When a potential difference is set up across opposite ends of a piece of metal or carbon, this haphazard exchange is ended and the free electrons are constrained to drift on average towards the positive pole of the applied potential. This drift, which is a relatively slow affair, constitutes an electric current and the material in which the drift occurs is an electrical conductor. *Figure 1.3* shows the probable path of an electron in a piece of copper wire before and after the application of an external voltage.

Electrons are not necessarily the only free charge carriers. Complete atoms are electrically neutral so their motion does not constitute an electric current. Atoms which are not complete by virtue of having lost one or more of their electrons, however, will exhibit an overall positive charge and are known as positive *ions*. So ions are not electrically neutral and, like electrons, they can act as charge carriers. When a voltage is applied across the medium in which the ions are present, a drift will occur in the direction of the negative pole. It is easily possible for electrons and ions to be on the move at the same time. In a gas, for example, electrons and positive ions can be moving in opposite directions under the influence of an impressed voltage; if the velocity acquired by the electrons becomes great enough, they may readily knock other electrons away from their parent atoms, so creating further positive ions. If the production of free electrons and ions builds up sufficiently in this way, the gas emits a coloured glow and is said to be *ionised*. You have only to look at night-time advertising displays to see this effect in action.

In metals, however, the only charge carriers are electrons, for the atoms, even when they have lost one or more of their valence electrons, are fixed rigidly within the atomic structure of the material.

At this point we must make a note of some importance. Since the charge carriers in metal conductors are negatively charged electrons, the movement of the carriers is in the direction negative to positive, that is, *opposite* to the *conventional* direction of current which you will have used throughout your work in electrical principles. The true *electronic* flow of current becomes of significance in the study of electronic devices.

Random movement of a free electron in a solid conductor

General drift of the electron towards a positive potential

Figure 1.3

THERMIONIC EMISSION

Provided that the temperature is low, for example, ordinary room temperature, the free electrons in a metal drift only from atom to atom *within* the conductor. None escapes from the surface of the conductor into the surrounding space. This is because of the strong attractive force exerted upon electrons located at or close to the surface by the mass of atoms making up the conductor. The movement of free electrons may, however, be accelerated by the addition of heat energy. If the temperature of the metal is raised, the free electrons gain velocity and hence kinetic energy. When the metal becomes sufficiently hot, some electrons acquire enough energy to break away from the surface of the conductor. The rate at which such *thermionic* (heat induced) emission occurs from the heated surface depends upon the material concerned and the temperature.

The escape of electrons cannot continue indefinitely. As soon as the emission begins, other factors come into play which tend to restrain the loss of electrons:

1. When the conductor loses electrons from its surface, the surface becomes positively charged and this tends to attract the electrons back again.

2. Electrons which have already escaped form a negative barrier which discourages other electrons from following their example.

3. The air molecules surrounding the heated surface intercept the escaping electrons and absorb most of their surplus energy in the collision. The result is that the electrons fall back to the surface under its positive attraction.

The effect of thermionic emission is put to use by enclosing the heated conductor in an evacuated envelope, usually a glass bulb having the necessary connections brought out through air tight seals. In the very near vacuum which can be achieved in such a bulb the problem of collision with air molecules is eliminated and the electrons can evaporate from the heated surface without restriction of that kind. The back attraction of the positive surface and the formation of a negative region made up from the cluster of electrons immediately in the vicinity of the surface remain unaffected, however. The result is that a negative cloud, or *space charge*, forms close to the heated surface and remains there, provided there is no change in the temperature, at a constant density. The reason for this is not difficult to see. Those electrons at the outer edge of the cloud, having lost their kinetic energy, want to return to the heated surface but are prevented from doing so by the rest of the electrons between them and the surface. At the inner edge of the cloud, individual electrons continually leave the surface but are replaced by others which have used up their energy in doing work against the established cloud and return. Once established, therefore, the density of the cloud remains substantially constant. *Figure 1.4* illustrates the formation of a space charge. The heated conductor from which electrons are released in this way is called a *cathode*.

The phenomenon of thermionic emission is put to use in all electronic valves and cathode ray tubes.

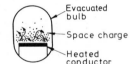

Evacuated bulb

Space charge

Heated conductor

Figure 1.4

CATHODES

The cathode is an essential part of any electronic valve because it provides the electrons necessary for the operation of the valve. Although many metals when heated sufficiently will supply electrons in the manner already described, only a few such metals are of practical use. The materials in general use are tungsten, thoriated tungsten and metals which have been coated with alkaline earth oxides such as calcium, strontium or barium.

For a given material the rate of emission of electrons depends only upon the temperature, and if a graph of emission current i is plotted against temperature, the general shape of the curve obtained will be as shown in *Figure 1.5*. The emission is small until a certain temperature T_1 is reached, after which it increases very rapidly. The temperature at which a pure metal will emit enough electrons to be of practical significance is very high, and tungsten is one of the few metals which will provide a copious supply of electrons without itself melting under the effects of the high temperature, a dazzling white heat of something like 2200 °C. Thoriated tungsten emitters are made from tungsten

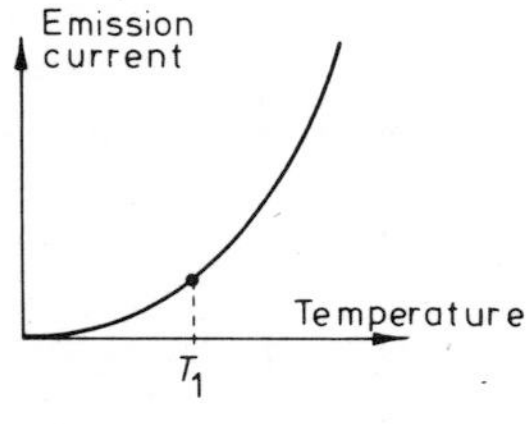

Emission current

Temperature

T_1

Figure 1.5

impregnated with thorium oxide. These emitters liberate electrons at a temperature of about 1700 °C, a bright yellow, and are much more economical of power than are the pure tungsten filaments. If alkaline earth oxides are applied as a coating to a nickel alloy base and dried, only a dull red heat of about 750 °C is sufficient to provide an abundant supply of emitted electrons. All the ordinary valves and cathode ray tubes you are likely to encounter will be operated from oxide coated cathodes.

The method of heating the cathode is used to distinguish between two different forms of cathode. The *directly heated* cathode is simply a wire mounted in an evacuated envelope and heated by the passage of an electric current (*Figure 1.6(a)*). The *indirectly heated* cathode consists of a thin walled metal sleeve or cylinder coated on the outside with alkaline earth oxide, while inside the sleeve is a coiled tungsten heating filament insulated electrically from the sleeve. This filament is used only for the purpose of heating the surrounding sleeve to the required temperature. It contributes nothing to the electron emission itself, which derives entirely from the coated surface of the sleeve. *Figure 1.6(b)* shows the construction. The assembly is, of course, mounted in an evacuated glass envelope.

The manner in which the emitted electrons are put to work will be discussed in due course. Here is another problem to think about.

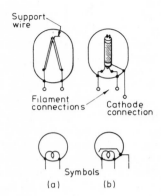

Support wire

Filament connections   Cathode connection

Symbols

(a)   (b)

Figure 1.6

(3) Would you agree that:
(a) an oxide coated cathode must be of indirectly heated form?
(b) a directly heated cathode has to be run considerably hotter than an indirectly heated one?
(c) a space charge, once established, prevents the emission of further electrons?

SEMICONDUCTORS

Certain materials are in the class of electrical conductors, characterised by a high density of free electrons. All metals, together with carbon, come into this category. Other materials have virtually no free electrons available and these are classified as non-conductors or *insulators*. Rubber, glass and mica are examples. Between these extremes come the *semiconductors*, materials which, under ordinary conditions, are neither good conductors nor good insulators but can be made to exhibit some of the properties of each. Among the semiconductors having practical importance in modern electronics are foremost the elements germanium and silicon, with selenium, lead sulphide, copper oxide and cadmium sulphide also having general and specialised applications.

To understand the nature of a semiconductor it is necessary to look into the atomic arrangement of *crystalline* substances. We have already talked about the structure of individual atoms, but not about the way an assemblage of atoms group together to form larger bodies. Certain materials form themselves into bodies called crystals which have characteristic geometric shapes. Materials which do not take such forms are non-crystalline or *amorphous*. It is not necessarily possible to distinguish one from another simply by looking at it. A sheet of glass is amorphous, but a slab of quartz, which may be polished to resemble glass, is crystalline. Crystal sizes vary enormously: a crystal of quartz takes the form of a hexagonal rod capped at each end by pyramids and may be many centimetres in length; a crystal of common table salt is a small rectangular block best seen under a good magnifying lens. Thin slabs or sections are cut from large crystals and put to a variety of electrical uses. Quartz crystals (incorrectly named), for example, are quartz *slices* used in microphones, pick-up heads and the like. So too, and of more concern to us, are wafers cut from germanium or silicon crystals and used in the manufacture of transistors and allied devices. Although carbon is a conductor, crystalline carbon is an insulator and a rather expensive one — diamond!

Inside a crystalline substance the outermost shell electrons (the valence electrons) of the individual atoms link up and arrange themselves with the valence electrons in adjacent atoms to form *co-valent bonds* which hold the atoms together in an orderly network or *lattice* structure. Thus, in any co-valent bond there are shared electrons, no atom having a monopoly in outermost electrons. Referring back to *Figure 1.2*, the arrangement of orbital electrons in a germanium atom in four shells is, reading from the inner K shell outwards, 2, 8, 18 and 4 electrons respectively; for the silicon atom the corresponding arrangement is 2, 8 and 4 electrons. It might appear that some or all of the four valence electrons in these atoms might easily be displaced from their orbits, to drift through the material as charge carriers under the influence of an applied voltage as they do in metals. In practice this does not happen; the valence electrons of each atom form co-valent bonds with neighbouring atoms and become very difficult to shift from their orbits. Crystals of pure germanium and pure silicon are therefore insulators, or at least extremely high value resistors. *Figure 1.7* is a two-dimensional representation of the effect of co-valent bonding. The valence electrons share themselves between four neighbouring atoms so that, in the case of germanium and silicon, the atoms behave as though each of their outer shells contain, not four, but eight electrons. In this condition the outer shell is in a stable state, there are no free electrons anywhere to act as charge carriers and the crystals are consequently electrical insulators. This situation is, of course, only true if the crystal structure is perfect and all the co-valent bonds are satisfied. There are always 'faults' and impurities present in the structure and these can provide free carriers so that perfect insulation is never possible.

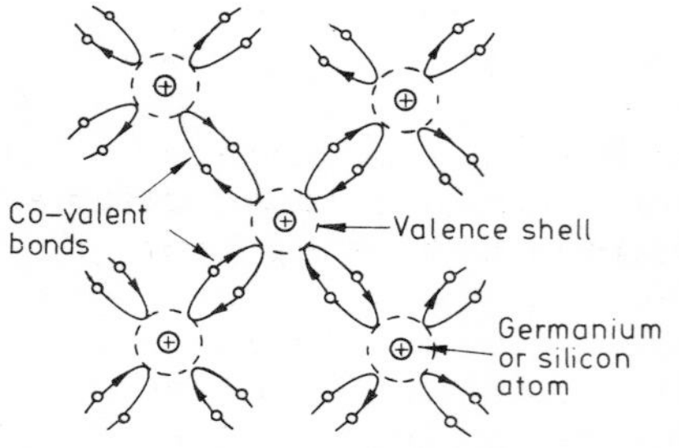

However, apart from this, if the temperature of germanium or silicon is raised, thermal agitation increases among the constituent atoms and some of the co-valent bonds are broken. Much of this goes on at ordinary room temperature, and the effect is accelerated as the temperature is raised above this level. This produces *thermally generated electrons* which act as negative charge carriers; so the crystal turns from a very good insulator into a poor conductor as its temperature is moderately raised. But the electrons are not the only charge carriers produced, unlike the case of thermionic emission from metals or ordinary electron movement in conducting wires. When a bond breaks and an electron is released, a vacancy or *hole* is left in the crystal structure. Since this hole has been formed by the removal of a negatively charged electron, the hole must have a positive charge associated with it. *Figure 1.8* illustrates the situation. The concept of positive hole charge carriers is, admittedly, a difficult one to appreciate, but you might consider it in this way: an electron is a basic

Co-valent bonds

Valence shell

Germanium or silicon atom

Each valence shell has effectively eight electrons—four of these come from the atom itself and four others come from four adjacent atoms

Figure 1.7

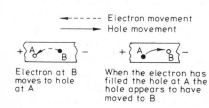

—————— Electron movement
——————► Hole movement

Electron at B moves to hole at A

When the electron has filled the hole at A the hole appears to have moved to B

Figure 1.8

negative charge so that when it moves out of a valence bond it leaves behind a hole which then manifests itself as a net positive charge. Under the influence of an applied voltage, the now free electrons move towards the positive pole of the supply but on the way many of them fill the vacancies they find in the structure. In this way, referring to the diagram, a hole disappears at A by being filled, but effectively reappears at B, the point recently vacated by the electron which filled it. In other words, an electron moving out of its valence bond into an adjacent hole can be looked upon as being equivalent electrically to the hole itself moving in the opposite direction. So while electrons move towards the positive pole of the supply, holes effectively move towards the negative pole. Both hole and electron movement contribute to conduction. Thermally generated electrons and holes always appear in pairs, and the resulting conductivity of the crystal is called the *intrinsic conductivity.*

IMPURITY ATOMS

Intrinsic semiconductor material is of little practical importance because, as we have seen, the conductivity is very temperature sensitive and the process of conduction is due partly to electrons and partly to holes. The preparation of the material to overcome these drawbacks involves changes in the conduction characteristics so that either electrons *or* holes become the dominant charge carriers. This is done by mixing an extremely small quantity (about one part in 100 million) of a selected impurity into the semiconductor material. The atoms of this impurity material must have dimensions roughly equal to those of germanium or silicon atoms so that they will fit into the crystal lattice without seriously upsetting the regular geometric construction. When the atoms of the impurity material have more valence electrons than are required to satisfy the valence bonds with neighbouring semiconductor atoms, there will be electrons 'left over', and these will be free to participate in current conduction. Such an impurity therefore will give the semiconductor material an abundance of negative charge carriers; it is then referred to as n-*type material* and electrons are the *majority carriers. Figure 1.9* is a simplified representation of such an impurity atom in part of a semiconductor crystal lattice. Here, each semiconductor atom has four valence electrons and the impurity atom has five. Four of the valence electrons of the impurity link with those of neighbouring semiconductor atoms to form co-valent bonds and so complete the crystal structure. The extra electron is free to move through the lattice. An impurity of this type is called a *donor* since it donates electrons as charge carriers. Examples of *n*-type impurities are antimony, arsenic and phosphorus. The atoms of these elements are *pentavalent*, i.e. they have five valence electrons.

Suppose now that the atoms of the impurity material have less valence electrons than are needed to satisfy the valence bonds in the semiconductor crystal (*Figure 1.10*). As before, each semiconductor atom has four valence electrons but the impurity atom has only three. Only three valence bonds with adjacent atoms therefore are satisfied, so that a hole accordingly appears in what would have been the fourth bond. Such an impurity therefore will give the semiconductor material an abundance of holes as charge carriers; we now have p-*type material* and positive holes are the majority carriers. This time the impurity

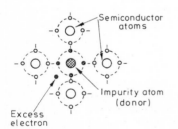

Figure 1.9

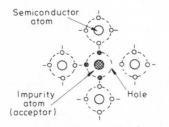

Figure 1.10

atoms are called *acceptors* because they can accept electrons from other atoms. Examples of *p*-type impurities are indium, aluminium and boron. The atoms of these elements are *trivalent*, that is, they have three valence electrons.

There is one point which you should be clear about at this stage. *n*- and *p*-type semiconductor materials have an electron 'excess' and an electron 'deficit' respectively, but the material is electrically neutral. You must not confuse the situation with electrostatic charges which can be built up on conductors or insulators; such charges represent a *displacement* of electrons from one part of a conductor to another, and such charges can be neutralised by contact with earth. Connecting a piece of *n*- or *p*-type material to earth will do nothing to remove the free electrons or fill the holes — if that happened there would be no such things as transistors!

One other thing before we turn to the practical applications of semiconductor material. Current moves more slowly through a semi-conductor than in a true conductor. The electrons drift more slowly because they encounter obstructions due to imperfections in the crystal lattice, and the movement of holes is even slower than that of electrons. This may sound startling at first, but remember that while electrons may occupy any position within the lattice between holes, the holes them-selves can only 'jump' from one valence bond to another — there are no intermediate positions at all.

Now here is your first set of problems. Not many to begin with, but although you are not expected to become atomic scientists, you will find some of the answers useful in your later work.

PROBLEMS FOR SECTION 1

(4) Complete the following statements:

(a) The particles found in an atomic nucleus are . . . . . . and . . . . . .

(b) An electron is about . . . . . . times 'lighter' than a proton.

(c) Electrons in the outermost shells of atoms are . . . . . . electrons.

(d) Only the . . . . atom has no neutron in its nucleus.

(e) The emission of electrons from a heated surface depends only upon the . . . . and the . . . .

(f) The majority carriers in p-type material are . . . .

(g) Increasing the temperature of a semiconductor crystal increases the . . . . and hence reduces the . . . .

(5) Say whether the following statements are true or false:

(a) All indirectly heated cathodes are oxide coated.

(b) The heating filament of an indirectly heated cathode may be fed from either a d.c. or an a.c. supply.

(c) A space charge once established, remains at a constant density even if the temperature of the surface is increased.

(6) Fill in the missing numbers in the following table:

	Protons	K	L	M	shells
Aluminium	13	2		3	
Silicon	14	2	8		
Phosphorus			8	5	
Chlorine	17	2	8		

(7) The gallium atom has four shells and its nucleus contains 31 protons. The K, L and M shells contain respectively 2, 8 and 18 electrons. Would gallium impurity atoms produce *p*-type or *n*-type semiconductor material?

(8) Eight valency electrons surround a silicon or a . . . . atom in a crystal of semiconductor material . . . . of these come from this atom and . . . . others come from . . . . adjacent atoms. Fill in the missing words.

2 Semiconductor and thermionic diodes

Aims: At the end of this Unit section you should be able to:
Explain the behaviour and action of minority charge carriers.
Understand the operation of a p-n *junction diode.*
Compare junction potentials of germanium and silicon diodes.
Plot and describe the static characteristics of germanium and silicon diodes.
Explain the operation of a thermionic diode.
Plot and describe the anode characteristics of thermionic diodes.

We have mentioned that intrinsic conduction in a semiconductor crystal does not depend upon the addition of impurity atoms. Temperature rise itself is sufficient to break many of the co-valent bonds in the crystal lattice, with the result that electron-hole pairs are created, each capable of acting as a charge carrier. We say that both charge carriers are *mobile*. The semiconductor crystal does not then behave as an insulator, as it would if all the bonds were complete and satisfied, but becomes a conductor, though not necessarily a particularly good one. As temperature increases more free charge carriers are produced as equal numbers of holes and electrons and the conductivity of the material rises. Hence the resistance of the crystal falls as the temperature rises, which means that the material has a negative temperature coefficient of resistance.

When a semiconductor crystal has been *doped* with impurity atoms as described in the previous section, the conduction which results is said to be by *extrinsic* action. In *n*-type material, mobile negative carriers (electrons) are produced without corresponding mobile positive carriers (holes). In *p*-type material, mobile positive carriers are produced without corresponding mobile negative carriers. This does not mean that an increase in temperature no longer leads to intrinsic action within the lattice. The production of hole-electron pairs still goes on but the extrinsic production of charged mobile carriers completely swamps out the intrinsic action. In the *p*-type, the relatively few extra holes produced are insignificant compared with the enormous number of holes already present. However, the extra electrons produced play an important part in the conduction process as these are *n*-carriers in *p*-type material. These electrons (and similarly for the relatively few holes found for the same reason in *n*-type material) are known as *minority carriers*. Under an impressed voltage, minority carriers move in the opposite direction to majority carriers, but their number depends upon temperature, not the added impurity atoms.

Extrinsic conduction is illustrated in *Figure 2.1*. You must bear in mind that only electrons can act as carriers in the external connecting wires. The flow of electrons in the *n*-type material of *Figure 2.1(a)* should not present you with any difficulty in understanding, but you may not find the concept of hole flow in the circuit of *Figure 2.1(b)* quite so obvious. It will help if you recall that in this case the movement

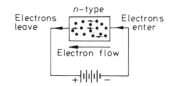

Figure 2.1(a)

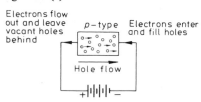

Figure 2.1(b)

of the holes through the crystal is equivalent to electrons moving in the opposite direction. Holes are filled (effectively disappear) at the right-hand side of the diagram as electrons enter from the negative pole of the battery; they surrender electrons (effectively appear) on the left-hand side of the diagram as the electrons return to the positive pole of the battery. In this way the holes move *only* through the semiconductor region of the circuit — their entrance on the left-hand side and exit on the right-hand side is all an illusion!

> (1) Does it make any difference to conduction which way round the batteries shown in *Figure 2.1* are connected?
> (2) Is the total current (as measured on an ammeter wired into the circuit) flowing through a piece of extrinsic semiconductor material less than, greater than or the same as the current would be if there were no minority carriers present?

THE JUNCTION DIODE

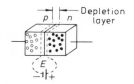

There is a recombination of holes and electrons in the vicinity of the junction

Figure 2.2

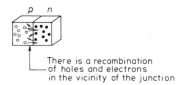

Figure 2.3

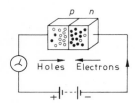

Figure 2.4(a)

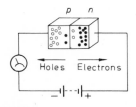

Figure 2.4(b)

If a piece of *n*-type silicon (or germanium) and a piece of *p*-type silicon (or germanium) are alloyed into contact as shown in *Figure 2.2*, the unit is called a *p-n* junction and exhibits properties which enable it to be used as a 'one-way' device or diode rectifier. The word diode stems from the fact that there are two parts or electrodes in the assembly. At the junction, electrons from the *n*-type silicon tend to diffuse into the *p*-type silicon, and holes from the *p*-type silicon tend to diffuse into the *n*-type silicon. In the immediate neighbourhood of the junction, therefore, holes and electrons recombine. Once recombined in this way they can take no further part in the conduction process. This small initial diffusion* of holes and electrons across the junction sets up what is called a *depletion layer* or *potential barrier*; the depletion layer having no majority carriers within its boundaries behaves as an insulator. Once established, this insulating layer prevents any further migration of either electrons or holes across the junction. The condition is equivalent to a source of potential (and hence an electric field) acting across the junction and may be represented as an imaginary battery *E* connected as shown in *Figure 2.3*. The *p*-side has gained electrons, the *n*-side has gained holes; the *p*-side must therefore become negative with respect to the *n*-side. The polarity of the battery is then as indicated. Note this very carefully. The actual voltage of the battery depends upon whether the junction material is silicon or germanium. Its value is about 0.3 V for germanium and 0.7 V for silicon, the exact value depending upon the carrier densities.

Now suppose that connections are made at the ends of the *n*- and *p*-type materials and that a voltage is applied from an external battery as shown in *Figure 2.4*. When the *p* region of the junction is made positive, as in *Figure 2.4(a)*, the holes are repelled by the positive field and the electrons by the negative field. Both holes and electrons are driven in the direction indicated by the arrows, towards the *p-n* junction where they recombine. A high current flows, since the junction barrier is

---

*If you add a small amount of dye to a jar of water and set it aside without stirring or other disturbance, the dye will be found to have diffused through the water within a matter of a few hours. Diffusion tends to equalise concentration throughout a system.

effectively removed and the resistance is consequently low. We say that the junction is biased in the forward direction.

When the *p* region is made negative, as in *Figure 2.4(b)*, holes are attracted by the negative field ²and electrons by the positive field. Both holes and electrons are drawn away from the *p-n* junction, the depletion layer is effectively widened, and the junction resistance becomes very high. As a result of this action, the current flow is very low. We say that the junction is reverse-biased. A *p-n* junction therefore is a one-way device, permitting current to flow in only one direction.

But here we must add a qualification to the last statement. You will have noticed that when the junction is biased in the reverse direction, the current flow is stated to be low, not zero. Why is this? Look again at *Figure 2.4*. In both diagrams the majority carriers are found in their respective halves of the junction: holes (open circles) and electrons (filled circles). But you will notice that a few electrons have been drawn in the *p*-regions, and a few holes in the *n*-regions. These are the minority carriers, generated remember, by thermal agitation of the co-valent bonds. When the junction is forward-biased as at (a) these minority carriers simply move along with the majority carriers and do nothing more than make a very small contribution to the relatively large current which is flowing in the circuit. When the junction is reverse-biased, however, as at (b), only the majority carriers are drawn away from the junction; the applied polarity is such that the minority carriers are attracted towards the junction. Hence a current flows in the circuit due entirely to the presence of the minority carriers. This current, which is normally extremely small, is called the *leakage current*. Notice that its direction is opposite to that of the large forward current which flows under forward bias conditions.

(3) If a junction diode is raised in temperature, what happens to (i) the forward current, (ii) the reverse leakage current — if anything?

You will have looked up the answer to the previous problem — after attempting it, of course. Raising the temperature causes a rapid increase in the generation of minority carriers and hence the leakage current. At around room temperature each increase of 10 °C roughly doubles the rate of generation for germanium, or of 5 °C for silicon. This might make it seem that germanium would be the better material to use where high ambient temperatures were concerned, but this is not so. Although the rate of increase is greater for silicon, its actual value at room temperature is considerably less than that of germanium — so silicon is used where high temperatures are likely to be encountered.

We require now a symbol for a semiconductor diode, and this is illustrated in *Figure 2.5*. When you use this symbol, keep in mind that the arrow points in the direction of the conventional flow of current through the diode. On this basis, the diode will conduct if the arrow is connected to the positive pole of the battery; it will not conduct if the arrow is connected to the negative pole of the battery. Many diodes look like small resistors and they are nearly always marked with a spot or coloured ring at one end. Such a marked end corresponds to the line

Figure 2.5

in the symbol, not the arrow, so this end has to be negative for the diode to conduct.

Characteristic Curves   If the temperature remains substantially constant, the only factor controlling the flow of current through a semiconductor diode is the applied voltage. If applied voltage and current are measured in a series of steps, the curve which results when the measured quantities are plotted as a graph is called the *static characteristic*. Static characteristic curves for germanium and silicon diodes are shown in *Figure 2.6* at (*a*) and (*b*) respectively. Forward voltage is plotted along the horizontal axes to the right of the origin and forward current is plotted vertically above the origin. This is the region in which the diodes conduct. Notice that the forward current does not become significant until the applied voltage is roughly equal to the barrier voltage set up at the depletion layer, about 0.3 V for germanium and 0.7 V for silicon, as already mentioned. After this, current rises very rapidly as the applied voltage increases. Clearly, the voltage cannot be increased indefinitely and the current cannot rise indefinitely; if this is attempted, the diode will be destroyed.

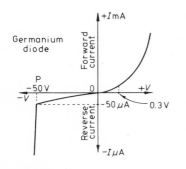

Figure 2.6(a)

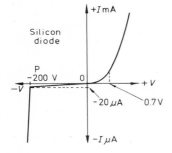

Figure 2.6(b)

The part of the curve to the left of and below the origin is the characteristic for a reverse-biased condition. The applied p.d. is now reversed ($-V$) and the current which flows is also reversed. This is simply the leakage current due to the minority carriers. Note the scaling of the vertical axes: forward current is in milliamperes, while reverse current is in microamperes. This scale change is necessary to show the curve of reverse current in detail. In the reverse direction the leakage current in the germanium diode tends to increase with voltage, whereas the silicon diode current is not only generally much smaller but tends to remain fairly constant. A point of particular significance appears at P on each curve, typically at about -50 V for germanium and -200 V for silicon, when the reverse current suddenly increases and builds up very rapidly to a high value. This effect is known as *avalanche breakdown* and unless the reverse current is limited in some way, results in the destruction of the diode. The reason for the avalanche breakdown is that if the reverse voltage becomes too great, the minority carriers are accelerated to the point where (a) they begin to heat up the diode, and (b) they collide with atoms in the depletion layer and dislodge further electrons, so creating further hole-electron pairs and hence more minority carriers. The effect 'avalanches' and rapidly results in a destructive flow of current.

(4) The leakage current of a certain germanium diode is 5 μA at 20 °C. What order of leakage current would you expect at 80 °C?

(5) Does a change in ambient temperature affect the value of reverse voltage at which a semiconductor diode will go into avalanche breakdown?

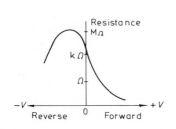

Figure 2.7

Figure 2.7 shows the static resistance characteristic of a semiconductor diode. As the forward voltage is increased, the resistance of the diode falls to a very low value. At decreasing values of forward voltage the resistance increases until, just above zero voltage, the depletion layer appears and the resistance becomes very high. As zero voltage is passed and reverse voltage is increased, the resistance reaches a peak value, and then decreases as the minority carriers begin to assume significant proportions.

> (6) Sketch a circuit suitable for plotting the static voltage-current and resistance curves of a semiconductor diode.

THE THERMIONIC DIODE

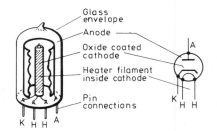

Figure 2.8

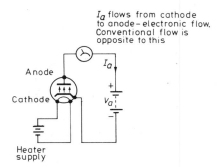

Figure 2.9

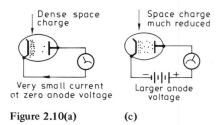

Figure 2.10(a)   (c)

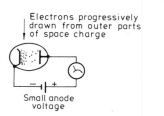

Figure 2.10(b)

The thermionic diode, or two-electrode valve, operates as a one-way device as does the *p-n* semiconductor diode. In appearance and in its mode of working it is completely different from the *p-n* diode. It consists of an emitter (the cathode) which in nearly all instances is in the form of a cylinder or sleeve, oxide coated and heated from an internal filament; and a collecting electrode (the anode) which takes the form of another cylinder axially surrounding the cathode sleeve. A general sketch of the construction is given in *Figure 2.8*, which shows also the symbol for a thermionic diode. The whole assembly is rigidly supported in an evacuated glass envelope.

A low voltage source is used to heat the filament which in turn heats the cathode sleeve to the proper operating temperature. Apart from this essential function, the heater filament is of no further interest. Electrons are emitted from the cathode and if the anode is maintained at a positive potential relative to the cathode, a current will flow between them and hence around the external parts of the circuit as indicated in *Figure 2.9*. Actually it will be found that a very small current flows even when the anode voltage (V_a) is zero. Recall that a space charge forms around the cathode and a highly negative region exists close to the cathode surface because of this. A few electrons on the outermost boundaries of the space charge are repelled strongly by this intensely negative field and find their way to the anode which is itself, with respect to the space charge, very slightly positive. These electrons then return to the cathode by way of the external circuit. *Figure 2.10(a)* shows this situation.

When the anode is made slightly positive, as in *Figure 2.10(b)*, electrons begin to be drawn from the outer fringes of the space charge, though at this stage no further electrons will be accepted from the cathode itself by the space charge. A negative region will still exist in front of the cathode face, even though the anode is now positive. The external current now increases accordingly. As the anode voltage is further increased (*Figure 2.10(c)*) the anode current will further increase, more and more electrons being drawn from the space charge. At the same time the space charge will reduce in density and effectively move towards the cathode, since the electrons closest to the anode are being progressively removed. All the time the space charge exists, the anode current (for a given anode voltage) is limited by what can be drawn from the outermost fringes of the charge, and the anode current is said to be space charge limited. It is important to appreciate this point. The number of electrons in transit at any instant is just sufficient to produce a negative space charge which shields from the attraction of the anode any electrons just then leaving the cathode. Anode current I_a depends therefore only upon V_a, being quite independent of the emission rate at the cathode.

As the anode voltage is increased still further, a point is reached

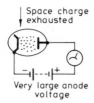

Space charge
exhausted

Very large anode
voltage

Figure 2.10(d)

when the rise in anode current slackens and there is no further increase in the current even though the anode voltage may be advanced indefinitely. In this state all the electrons emitted by the cathode are being collected by the anode, the space charge now having ceased to exist. I_a has now reached its maximum possible value for the particular cathode temperature established. The diode is then said to be saturated or temperature limited. *Figure 2.10(d)* shows the situation where the emitted electrons move directly to the anode without spending some of their time in an intervening space charge.

Like the *p-n* junction diode, the thermionic diode conducts only in one direction: when the anode is positive with respect to the cathode. If the polarity is reversed, no anode current is possible.

Characteristic Curves

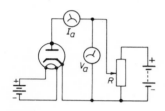

Figure 2.11

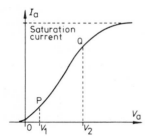

Figure 2.12

A circuit suitable for obtaining a series of related values of V_a and I_a is sketched in *Figure 2.11*. The potentiometer R is advanced in steps of, say, 5 V, from zero to a maximum dictated by the particular diode, and readings of I_a are recorded at each step. A graph then can be plotted showing the variation in I_a as V_a is advanced. Such a curve is drawn in *Figure 2.12*. This figure shows that between the points marked P and Q the characteristic is substantially straight. This being so, the diode is behaving for anode voltages between the limits V_1 and V_2 as a linear resistance, I_a being directly proportional to V_a. Beyond Q the curve bends over as saturation sets in. The small initial bend between the origin and point P is exaggerated for clarity; it is usually much less marked than the figure indicates. No reverse voltage characteristic is given as the current remains at zero for all anode voltages below zero.

For the correct cathode temperature, i.e. for the heater voltage set to the manufacturer's specification, it is not normally possible to run the diode into the saturation region of the characteristic, and diodes are never used in this region. It is, however, possible to obtain saturation region characteristics experimentally by deliberately reducing the heater voltage and hence the cathode temperature. The circuit of *Figure 2.11* can be used for this, with the addition of a suitable variable resistor of a few ohms value connected in series with the heater. By underrunning the heater by 50% and 75% of its normal operating voltage, the cathode emission is reduced sufficiently for saturation to begin at relatively low values of anode voltage, and in this way it is possible to obtain curves similar to those shown in *Figure 2.13*.

COMPARISONS

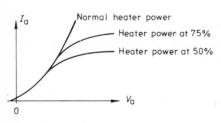

Figure 2.13

Both the semiconductor and the thermionic diode do the same electrical job — they perform as one-way devices. Once the thermionic diode reigned supreme, but it has now almost universally been replaced by the semiconductor. This is because the semiconductor diode requires no heater supply so there is no wasted electrical and thermal energy, and therefore no ventilation problems. Also it is very compact, robust, and can be made to handle large currents without excessive voltage loss because of its very low forward resistance. On the other hand it has the problem of leakage current when reverse-biased, so that the reverse resistance is not infinitely great (as it is in the thermionic diode), and reverse breakdown occurs at a much lower voltage than it does in the thermionic diode.

In the next Unit section we shall look into the applications of diodes. Before that, here are some test problems.

PROBLEMS FOR SECTION 2

Group 1

(7) Explain the meanings of the following terms: (i) valence electron, (ii) hole, (iii) impurity atom, (iv) leakage current, (v) avalanche breakdown.

(8) Fill in the missing words:

(a) The space charge is densest near the . . . .

(b) A thermionic diode biased in the forward direction should be operated only in the . . . . region.

(c) Comparing germanium and silicon diodes, the . . . . voltage is higher but the . . . . current is lower in the silicon diode.

(d) For a given cathode material, thermionic emission depends only upon the . . . .

(e) When a semiconductor diode is forward biased, the leakage current flows in the . . . . direction . . . . . the main current.

(9) Are the following statements true or false:

(a) A semiconductor diode has two junctions.

(b) In a semiconductor diode, it is the majority carriers that diffuse across the junction.

(c) Leakage current in the circuit wires connected to a semiconductor diode consists only of holes.

(d) The reverse current in a germanium diode is very much greater than in a silicon diode.

(e) In *p*-type material a large number of holes = a small number of electrons + a large number of negatively ionised acceptor atoms.

(10) The current in a thermionic diode is first space charge limited and then temperature limited. Explain the meaning of this statement.

(11) The leakage current in a certain silicon diode is 0.05 μA at 25 $^{\circ}$C. What will be its approximate value at 100 $^{\circ}$C?

(12) After the method illustrated in *Figure 2.7*, sketch a resistance/voltage curve for a thermionic diode.

(13) What properties would you expect a perfect diode to exhibit? If there was such a device as a perfect diode, what would its characteristic curve look like? Make a sketch.

(14) Which electrode, anode or cathode, of a thermionic diode corresponds to the *n*-region of a *p-n* junction diode?

(15) The performance of a semiconductor diode is affected by increases in the ambient temperature. Do you think this statement is also true of thermionic diodes?

(16) Sketch a typical characteristic curve for a *p-n* junction diode, and explain its appearance from the movement of the carriers concerned.

Group 2

(17) The two diodes shown in *Figure 2.14* can be assumed to have zero forward resistance and infinite reverse resistance. Calculate the currents in each branch of the circuit (i) with the battery connected as shown, (ii) with the battery reversed.

(18) The width of the depletion layer (which may be assumed to be a perfect insulator) depends upon the applied reverse

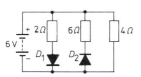

Figure 2.14

voltage. Can you think of any practical application to which this effect might be put?

(19) At the avalanche breakdown point of a semiconductor diode, the voltage across the diode ($-V$) is practically constant, irrespective of the current flowing through the diode. Look back at *Figure 2.6*. Ignoring the possibility of burn-out for the moment, can you think of any practical application of this effect?

(20) A thermionic diode has the following characteristics

V_a (V)	0	10	20	30	40	50	60	70	80	90	100
I_a (mA)	0	1.0	2.5	4.1	6.0	8.2	10.4	12.9	15.3	18.4	21.7

Plot the characteristic curve neatly on graph paper. This diode is connected in series with a 500 Ω resistor and a d.c. supply (forward biased). Find (i) the current flowing, (ii) the p.d. across the circuit, when the p.d. across the diode is 65 V.

(21) A voltage increases uniformly from zero to 100 V in a time of 1 s. This voltage is applied to terminals A and B of the circuit shown in *Figure 2.15*. Assuming that the diode has a constant forward resistance of 50 Ω and an infinite reverse resistance, sketch the voltage waveform you would expect to obtain at terminals C and D during the 1 s rise.

(22) A thermionic diode is connected to a 50 V battery, anode positive, and a current of 10 mA flows in the circuit. Where is the power represented by the product of voltage and current being dissipated?

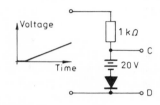

Figure 2.15

3 Applications of semiconductor diodes

Aims: At the end of this Unit section you should be able to:
Discuss the basic application of semiconductor diodes to power rectifier circuits.
Understand the action of a Zener diode as a voltage stabiliser and overload protector.
Understand the operation of a Varactor diode.
Explain the meaning and significance of peak inverse voltage.
Explain the purpose and operation of simple smoothing circuits.

We have now dealt in some detail with the theory of both thermionic and semiconductor diodes. Some of the more common applications of diodes will now be considered, and in Unit Section 9 further applications in the field of logic circuits will be discussed. In the applications which follow, where non-specialised diode elements are concerned, bear in mind that the circuit actions described are exactly the same irrespective of whether thermionic or semiconductor diodes are being employed. We shall, however, deal throughout with semiconductor elements only, as the thermionic diode is now little used in electronics.

RECTIFIER CIRCUITS

A rectifier is a device by which a direct current can be obtained from an alternating voltage supply, and the process of such a conversion is called *rectification.*

As you will have learned from your Electrical Principles programme, an alternating current is one which flows first in one direction along a conductor and then, after a given time, reverses and flows for a further period of time in the opposite direction. As we recall, such a complete backwards and forwards movement of the charge carriers (electrons only in this case) constitutes one cycle of the alternating current. *Figure 3.1* shows examples of alternating currents. On the other hand,

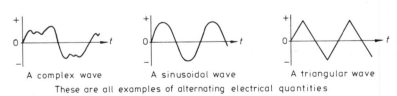
A complex wave   A sinusoidal wave   A triangular wave
These are all examples of alternating electrical quantities

Figure 3.1

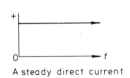
A steady direct current

Figure 3.2(a)

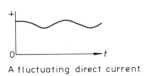
A fluctuating direct current

Figure 3.2(b)

a direct current is one which flows always in one definite direction, though it is not necessarily a steady or constant current. A current flowing from the positive to the negative terminal of a well charged battery through some form of resistance or load is generally a steady flow, maintaining a certain level for the whole length of time that the circuit is operating. The curve of such a current is shown in *Figure 3.2(a)*. In *(b)* a fluctuating direct current is illustrated. At first glance this might be confused with an alternating current, but in this diagram the current never crosses the horizontal axis. Electrons in this circuit move in a cyclic manner, but they never turn around and move backwards.

Almost all electronic equipment operates from steady direct current supplies. In many instances such supplies are obtained from cells or batteries: portable radios, pocket calculators and flashlamps are familiar examples. But we do not normally operate our television receivers from battery supplies, and certainly it would not be very practicable to operate, say, large computer systems or high power transmitters from batteries. We use the mains electricity supply for such purposes, hence it becomes necessary to convert the alternating current (or voltage) of this supply into the direct current (or voltage) that our apparatus requires.

The simplest type of rectifier is a circuit element which performs the function of an automatic switch. A perfect rectifier would have zero resistance one way and infinite resistance the other, and the rectifier circuits we are going to examine will be assumed to have perfect rectifier elements. Clearly, our one-way *p-n* junction diode will serve the purpose of a rectifier element.

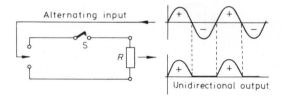

Figure 3.3

To convert the sinusoidal alternating current flowing in resistor *R* of *Figure 3.3* into a one-way or unidirectional current it is necessary to eliminate one half or other of the alternations. The curve must lie wholly above the horizontal axis or wholly below it, but it must not cross it. The obvious solution is to switch the circuit off whenever the current is about to reverse. If switch S is closed for each positive half-cycle of input current and opened for each negative half-cycle, the resulting current flow through *R* will be a series of positive pulsations, that is, a current which continually goes on and off but never reverses in direction. It is true we are using only one half of each input cycle and the unidirectional current we are getting as our output is a long way from being the steady current we require, but the method nevertheless provides us with a starting point from which we can now develop a number of rectifier systems.

THE HALF-WAVE RECTIFIER

The circuit of a half-wave rectifier is shown in *Figure 3.4*. This includes a transformer (as will all the circuits to be discussed) which is used for two basic reasons: it isolates the equipment being supplied from direct connection to the mains supply and so increases safety, and it enables the mains voltage to be either increased or decreased to a level suited to the apparatus for which the rectified supply will be finally required. It is not directly associated with the process of rectification which is our present concern. We are interested only in the fact that an alternating voltage is present at the secondary terminals A and B.

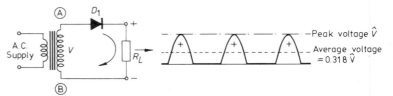

Figure 3.4

When terminal A is positive with respect to B, the diode conducts. The positive half-cycle of voltage across A–B therefore causes a current to flow around the circuit and a voltage will be developed across the load resistor R_L corresponding to the form of the half-cycle wave. When the input polarity reverses, terminal A will be negative with respect to B and the diode will switch off.

The voltage developed across R_L thus consists of half-sinewaves, and the circuit is known as a *half-wave rectifier*. The current through R_L is always in one direction, as shown, in spite of the on-off fluctuations; so our output is unidirectional. Notice that the peak value of the output wave is equal to the peak value of the alternating input voltage from the transformer, $\hat{V}$. You will also recall that the average value of the output wave is $\hat{V}/\pi$ or about 0.318 $\hat{V}$, shown in the broken line in *Figure 3.4*.

THE FULL-WAVE RECTIFIER

The half-wave rectifier has the disadvantage that there is no output at all for half of the available input. The full-wave rectifier, as its name implies, enables us to use both half-cycles of the input wave. The circuit is shown in *Figure 3.5*. Two diodes are used now, together with a transformer whose secondary winding is centre tapped at C. We can treat the centre tap as being a neutral point so that terminals A and B swing alternately positive and negative about it. Each diode consequently conducts in turn when its particular anode happens to be positive with respect to the centre point C. What we really have is two half-wave rectifier circuits connected to a single load resistor R_L, and each of these 'part' circuits take it in turn to supply current to the load. Following the direction of current flow as the diagram indicates, we notice that the current through R_L is, for both diode circuits, in the same direction. The output voltage developed across R_L is therefore unidirectional, the spaces between the half-sinewaves developed by either diode section now being filled in by the other diode section. The average output voltage across the load is now double that of the half-wave rectifier circuit, that is, about 0.636 $\hat{V}$. The peak voltage of the output wave is, as before, equal to the peak value of the alternating input voltage from *each half* of the secondary winding. Having to use the double winding on the transformer makes this component more bulky in size and of course more expensive.

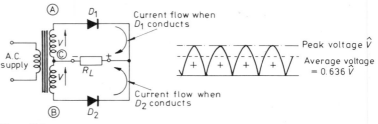

Figure 3.5

THE BRIDGE RECTIFIER

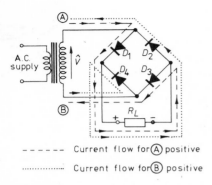

- - - - - Current flow for Ⓐ positive
············· Current flow for Ⓑ positive

Figure 3.6

This form of full-wave rectifier uses four diodes but does not require a centre tapped transformer. As diodes are much cheaper components than transformers, this circuit is less expensive and often less bulky than the two-diode full-wave rectifier.

The circuit of the bridge rectifier is shown in *Figure 3.6*. This time the diodes conduct in series-pairs. When secondary terminal A is positive with respect to B, diodes D_1 and D_3 conduct in series, but diodes D_2 and D_4 are switched off. When the input polarity reverses, D_2 and D_4 switch on in series, but D_1 and D_3 switch off. Following the current direction through in each case, you will see that the current flow through load R_L is always in one direction as indicated. Once again a unidirectional current is obtained and so the voltage developed across R is unidirectional. As for the two-diode full-wave rectifier, the average output voltage is 0.636 $\hat{V}$.

Go through the above description carefully and make sure you understand the working of the bridge rectifier, as it has many applications in electronics.

PRACTICAL DIODE RATINGS

Certain voltage and current ratings are of importance in connection with rectifiers, and now that we have dealt with the three rectifier circuits commonly found, we shall illustrate these rating factors by referring them to the circuits concerned.

Power Dissipation

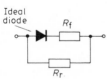

Figure 3.7

The ideal or perfect diode element we have so far assumed does not dissipate any power. In the forward direction its resistance is zero, hence whatever current flows through it, the voltage developed across it must be zero. In the reverse direction its resistance is infinite, hence whatever voltage is developed across it, the current flowing through it must be zero. In both cases, the power dissipated is zero. In the real-life diode, however, the forward resistance is never zero and the reverse resistance is never infinite, so power must be dissipated within the element.

An *equivalent circuit* for a practical diode can be obtained by assuming that we have a perfect element, but connected in series with this is a small value resistor R_f representing the actual forward resistance, and connected in parallel is a large value resistor R_r representing the reverse resistance. The circuit is shown in *Figure 3.7*. You will encounter equivalent circuit representation of this sort throughout your electronics programme. When a voltage is applied in the forward direction to this circuit the apparent resistance of the device is very closely equal to R_f, while reverse voltage can send current only through R_r, the ideal element itself cutting off R_f completely. So power is dissipated in these resistive components of the real semiconductor diode in both the forward and the reverse directions of applied voltage. This dissipation will appear in the form of heat at the junction. It is necessary to ensure that this local heating does not lead to an appreciable rise in temperature and so to an appreciable increase in the leakage current across the junction. Failure to do this may well lead to the destructive 'avalanche' effect mentioned in the previous Unit section, even though the diode is nowhere close to its reverse voltage breakdown point. For this reason, rectifier diodes intended for use in high current circuits are made with thick based metal cases provided with fixing studs which enable them to be bolted down to large area metal plates which then act as so-called *heat sinks* and permit the heat to be rapidly conducted away from the junction. A typical high power rectifier diode element is shown in *Figure 3.8.*

Peak Inverse Voltage

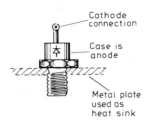

Figure 3.8

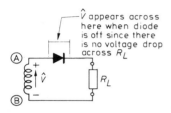

Arrows indicate instantaneous direction of voltage

Figure 3.9(a)

There are two important and related factors which have to be considered in the design of rectifier circuits in addition to the problem of power dissipation: these are the reverse breakdown point of the diode, and the *peak* operational voltage present across the diode when it is non-conducting. A rectifier diode must, of course, operate well away from its breakdown point, and here the main objective of the diode manufacturer is to ensure that breakdown occurs at far greater reverse voltages than the device will normally be subjected to in use. A rectifier diode must therefore be used only in a circuit where the applied reverse voltage is never of sufficient amplitude to approach the breakdown point. The value of the breakdown voltage for a particular diode is quoted by the manufacturer under the heading of the *peak inverse voltage* (p.i.v.).

Peak inverse voltage is the maximum voltage appearing across the terminals of a rectifier and acting in the reverse direction. The figure quoted for the p.i.v. usually implies that it represents the maximum reverse voltage that may be applied to the diode without reverse breakdown occurring, and this is the sense in which we will use the term.

We shall reconsider the three rectifier circuits already covered in terms of the peak inverse voltages present across the diodes, and for convenience the diagrams are reproduced in skeleton form in *Figure 3.9.*

In the case of the half-wave rectifier at (*a*), when the diode is reverse biased and switched off, no current flows in R_L, hence the applied voltage appears solely across the diode. The p.i.v. is therefore equal to $\hat{V}$, the peak value of the transformer secondary output. This means that the diode breakdown voltage must be greater in this case than $\hat{V}$, *not* the r.m.s. value of voltage in which the transformer output will be normally stated.

> (1) A diode has a p.i.v. rating of 300 V. Could this diode be used as a half-wave rectifier with a transformer having a stated secondary voltage of 250 V?

Consider now the full-wave circuit shown at (*b*). At the instant when terminal A is at its maximum positive swing, diode D_1 will be fully conducting and the voltage across the load resistor R_L will be $\hat{V}$ with the polarity indicated. The voltage between points C and B will also be $\hat{V}$ and C will be positive with respect to B. Hence, as far as diode D_2 (which is reverse biased at this time) is concerned, it has across its terminals the load voltage in series with the voltage across CB. These two voltages are aiding each other, hence they combine to give a total reverse voltage across D_2 of $2\,\hat{V}$. The p.i.v. in this case is therefore twice the peak voltage on either half of the transformer secondary. As the full-wave two-diode rectifier is in very common use, this aspect of the p.i.v. present on the diodes must be carefully kept in mind.

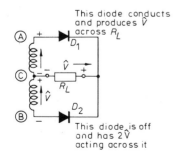

Figure 3.9(b)

> (2) A mains transformer is rated as giving an output of 350 V on each half of its secondary winding. What will be the p.i.v. across the diodes used in a full-wave circuit with this transformer?

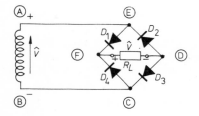

Figure 3.9(c)

Turning now to the bridge rectifier shown in (*c*), we take again the instant when the applied voltage is at its peak value and terminal A is positive. The voltage across the load resistor will be $\hat{V}$ with the polarity shown, diodes D_1 and D_3 now conducting. If we follow around the circuit AEDFCB through series diodes D_2 and D_4 which are now reverse biased and switched off, we see that the load voltage adds to the transformer voltage to give (as in the previous case) a total of $2\,\hat{V}$. This time, however, the voltage is shared between diodes D_2 and D_4 in series, hence the p.i.v. per diode is simply $\hat{V}$.

SMOOTHING CIRCUITS

The pulsating output we obtain from the rectifier circuits so far discussed is not suitable as it stands for the operation of equipment which requires a steady d.c. supply such as we should obtain from batteries. To iron out the rough outputs, as it were, smoothing circuit networks are connected to the rectifiers. The most simple case is illustrated in *Figure 3.10*, which shows a half-wave rectifier with a *reservoir capacitor*

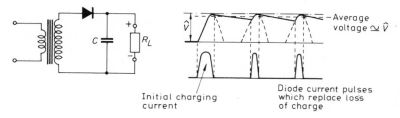

Figure 3.10

connected across the load. This capacitor is of large capacity, generally within the range 10–100 μF, or even greater. Consider what happens during the first positive output half-cycle after switching on. The capacitor will charge up to the peak value of the rectifier output voltage, that is, to $\hat{V}$. During the interval represented by the missing negative half-cycle of output no further charge is added to C and the voltage across its terminals falls slightly as it discharges through R_L. However, provided the discharge is relatively slow, which in effect is the same thing as saying that the value of R_L is large, the fall in terminal voltage before the arrival of the next positive half-cycle is very small. The capacitor is then 'topped-up' by the tip of this half-cycle, and the process then continues for the whole of the time that the circuit is switched on. You will notice two important points: (a) the waveform shown in full line is very much smoother than it was before the capacitor was added, (b) the average voltage across the load resistor is much greater. The best smoothing effect is obtained when the value of R_L is extremely high, for then there is negligible discharge between the output half-cycles and the almost steady d.c. output approximates in amplitude to $\hat{V}$. When the load resistor is small, however, the discharge becomes large and the output voltage is again rippled, though not to such a severe extent as that of an unsmoothed supply. The greater the capacity of the capacitor, for a given value of R_L, the better the smoothing. The product of C and R_L is called the *time constant* of the circuit.

One further important point must now be discussed. Once the capacitor is charged, the output voltage is, on average, approximately equal to $\hat{V}$. Suppose that it is equal to 0.9 $\hat{V}$. This means that it is providing a voltage which is acting in opposition to the voltage provided by the transformer secondary winding on the positive half-cycles during which the diode normally conducts. The diode cannot conduct, however, until its anode voltage becomes greater than the voltage on its cathode. If the voltage on the cathode is, for our illustrative example, $0.9\hat{V}$, then the diode remains switched off until the positive swing at transformer terminal A exceeds this value. The diode, therefore, now conducts over only a small part of each positive half-cycle from the transformer, whereas without the inclusion of capacitor C, it conducted over each complete half-cycle. The lower graph of *Figure 3.10* shows the corresponding pulsations of diode current. There are two dangers here for the unwary builder of a rectifier unit with added smoothing. The period during which the diode is conducting is a very small fraction of a cycle, and during this time it has to supply to the capacitor all the charge lost during the remainder of the cycle. The surge of current can therefore be very large, and hence the power dissipation in the diode can be considerable, even though its forward resistance may be small. Further, since the capacitor retains most of its charge between cycles, the voltage across the load resistor adds to the inverse voltage of the supply during the negative half-cycle when the diode is reverse biased. The p.i.v. in a half-wave rectifier is therefore almost equal to twice the peak transformer voltage, i.e. double the value it reaches in the absence of the smoothing capacitor. The diode chosen for the job must be rated to withstand this.

(3) A diode has a forward resistance of R_f ohms and a reverse resistance which may be considered infinite. It is used in a circuit similar to that shown in *Figure 3.4*. Sketch a graph of the output variations of current through the load resistor R_L. If the transformer peak output voltage is $\hat{V}$, write down expressions for (a) the average current, (b) the r.m.s. current in the load*.

THE ZENER DIODE

You will recall that under reverse bias conditions, the only current flow in a *p-n* diode circuit is that due to minority carriers passing across the depletion layer. In an ideal diode this current would be zero, but in a real diode it is present though normally very small at ordinary temperatures: a matter of a few microamperes for a germanium diode and a mere nanoampere (10^{-9} A) or so for a silicon element. As the reverse bias is increased there is little effect on the flow of minority carriers, particularly in silicon diodes, and the typical characteristic shown in *Figure 3.11* shows that an almost constant reverse current flows. However, if the reverse voltage is continually increased, the point of breakdown is eventually reached and the current increases very suddenly.

We can now examine in a little more detail the mechanism of the breakdown or avalanche effect. *Figure 3.12* shows part of the crystal lattice of the semiconductor material, with four atomic nuclei each with its four valence electrons. With a sufficiently high reverse voltage, an electron E_1 is accelerated through the lattice with enough velocity to dislodge a valence electron E_2. This electron now comes under the

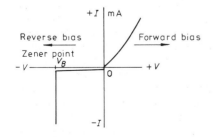

Figure 3.11

*We are dealing with a non-sinusoidal waveform when we consider current. It can be proved that the r.m.s. value of the rectified waveform current is $\hat{I}/2$.

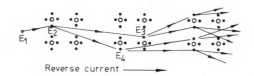

Figure 3.12

influence of the applied field and is similarly accelerated. In turn, these two electrons collide with further valence electrons E_3 and E_4 and break the co-valent bonds. There are now four electrons to continue the effect of dislodging further electrons and so build up what quickly becomes an avalanche of electrons throughout the lattice. If the breakdown is uncontrolled, the diode will be destroyed in an extremely short time, but damage can be prevented by connecting a resistance of a suitable value in series with the diode. At the point of breakdown, the maximum avalanche current can then never exceed the current determined by the resistor, and this current can be limited to a value which makes overheating and damage to the diode impossible.

Now it might seem that the best thing to do in any design incorporating semiconductor diodes would be to make sure (as we have emphasised for the rectifier circuits) that the reverse voltage was never great enough to get anywhere near the breakdown point. This is true for diodes used as rectifiers, but there are other diode applications which actually make use of the avalanche condition. Such diodes are known as *Zener diodes* or *voltage regulator diodes*. These diodes are deliberately connected into a circuit in the reverse direction, that is, the cathode terminal is connected to the positive pole of the supply and the anode to the negative pole. The diode is then reverse biased and avalanche is possible as soon as the applied voltage reaches an appropriate level.

Look again at *Figure 3.11.* Notice that after breakdown, the voltage across the diode remains virtually constant at the level V_B in spite of the increasing current flowing through it. This means that provided the avalanche current is prevented from becoming destructively great, we can use such a device as a source of constant voltage. Such Zener diodes are available with a wide range of breakdown voltages, from about -2 V down to some -200 V, the actual characteristic being determined by the impurity concentrations introduced during manufacture. They are also made in a range of power handling capabilities from half a watt or so up to many watts. The symbol for a Zener diode is shown in *Figure 3.13.*

We shall now look at one or two applications of the Zener diode.

Anode   Cathode

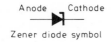

Zener diode symbol

Figure 3.13

THE ZENER STABILISER

The circuit requirements of a simple Zener diode voltage stabiliser are remarkably simple: apart from the diode itself, which is a very inexpensive device, only one resistor is necessary. If we cast our minds back to the rectifier and smoothing circuits discussed earlier, it is clear that some ripple always remains on the output voltage, and that this becomes more pronounced as the current drawn from the reservoir capacitor by the load increases. This in turn reduces the average output voltage. In cases where the current drawn from the power unit is substantially constant there is no particular problem, but where the current is liable to wide variation, such as additional loads being switched into and out of circuit, changes in the output voltage can cause very serious problems.

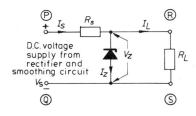

Figure 3.14

The circuit of a simple Zener stabiliser is shown in *Figure 3.14*. This is connected to the output of a power supply unit at terminals P and Q. Resistor R_s is connected in series with the Zener and provides the necessary protection against excessive current flow at the breakdown point. The resistor R_L represents, as usual, the load connected across the diode; this could be a small amplifier, for example, or perhaps an electric motor for a model. Notice how the diode is connected: its cathode goes to the positive terminal of the d.c. supply, hence it is reverse biased and under proper application will be operating in the breakdown condition.

To understand the action of the circuit, the Zener diode can be considered as a reservoir of current so long as it remains broken down. It then responds to variations in both the supply voltage at terminals P and Q, and the load current I_L flowing through R_L as follows:

1. Suppose the d.c. output voltage at P-Q increases for some reason, then the current through the Zener increases while the increase in voltage appears across R_s – *not* across the Zener. The Zener voltage, remember, remains at its breakdown value V_z, irrespective of the increase in current through it. Similarly, if the d.c. output at P-Q decreases, the Zener surrenders the extra current and the voltage across R_s falls. So the variation is 'absorbed' by series resistor R_s and the output voltage at R-S remains constant.

2. If the load current I_L increases for any reason, the Zener current decreases by the same amount. Similarly, if the load current decreases, the Zener current increases by the same amount. This time, the Zener takes up any excess current and sheds any current difference demanded by the load, so acting as a current reservoir while maintaining a constant voltage at terminals R-S.

There is a minimum Zener current for which the voltage stabilisation is effective and the Zener current must never be permitted to fall below this. In other words, the Zener must be in its breakdown condition at all times. This minimum current is a function of the voltage across the Zener and so this condition represents the minimum value of the applied d.c. voltage permissible. Zeners can stabilise satisfactorily down to currents of the order of 0.5 mA or so. The upper limit of current is, of course, dependent upon the power rating of the device.

The following examples are worked for you and illustrate the action of stabiliser circuits in actual figures. You need nothing more than Ohm's law as your mathematical equipment to be able to cope with problems on simple Zener stabilisers.

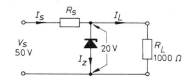

Figure 3.15

Example (4). A 20 V stabilised supply is required from a 50 V d.c. input. A 20 V Zener diode is to be used, having a power rating of 2 W. Find the required value of the series resistor R_s.

The basic circuit of the stabiliser is shown in *Figure 3.15*. Now we have to protect the Zener by making sure that the greatest current flowing through it at its rated breakdown voltage of 20 V does not exceed its power rating of 2 W. The greatest current will flow through the Zener when the load current I_L is zero (or if the load is disconnected). Hence

$$\text{Maximum current} = \frac{\text{Watts}}{\text{Voltage}} = \frac{2}{20} = 0.1 \text{ A}$$

To stabilise at 20 V from a 50 V input, the voltage drop across R_s must be 30 V. Hence

$$R_s = \frac{30}{0.1} = 300 \,\Omega$$

Example (5). If the Zener diode of the previous example stabilises down to a current of 1 mA, calculate the greatest and least supply voltage input between which stabilisation is obtained. The load resistance R_L is 1000 Ω.

For the greatest supply voltage (V_s) the Zener will pass its maximum current of 0.1 A. Then, referring to the figure, and working in milliamps

$$I_L = \frac{20}{1000} = 20 \,\text{mA}$$

But

$$I_s = I_z + I_L$$

$$\therefore \; I_s = 100 + 20 = 120 \,\text{mA}$$

Hence

$$\text{Maximum } V_s = (120 \times 10^{-3} \times 300) + 20 \,\text{V}$$

$$= 56 \,\text{V}$$

For the least supply voltage, the Zener must pass 1 mA. Hence

$$I_L = 20 \,\text{mA, as before}$$

and

$$I_s = I_z + I_L = 1 + 20 = 21 \,\text{mA}$$

Hence

$$\text{Minimum } V_s = (21 \times 10^{-3} \times 300) + 20 \,\text{V}$$

$$= 26.3 \,\text{V}$$

Notice the wide variation possible in the voltage supply, i.e. 26.3 V to 56 V, over which the output voltage to the load remains constant at 20 V.

Example (6). Suppose the voltage supply V_s in the previous example is 50 V. What will be the minimum possible value to which the load resistance can be reduced if stabilisation is to remain effective?

When R_L is reduced, the load current I_L increases and I_z

correspondingly falls. I_z must not fall below 1 mA, however, so for this condition

$$I_s = \frac{30}{300} = 0.1\,\text{A}\ (100\,\text{mA})$$

as for Example (4). Then

$$I_L = 100 - 1 = 99\,\text{mA}$$

$$\therefore R_L = \frac{20}{99 \times 10^{-3}} = 202\,\Omega$$

ZENER PROTECTION

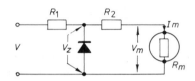

Figure 3.16

Another application of Zener diodes is shown in *Figure 3.16*, which shows a method of protecting a sensitive meter or similar apparatus against accidental overload. Suppose the meter has a full scale deflection (f.s.d.) current I_m and that at this current the voltage developed across the instrument is V_m. Resistors R_1 and R_2 are then selected in conjunction with the Zener characteristics so that if the applied voltage V exceeds V_m, the excess current resulting will be bypassed through the diode and not through the meter. This can be arranged by ensuring that when V equals V_m the Zener just breaks down but draws only a negligible current. At this time the meter must, of course, just indicate its f.s.d.

Always work problems of the kind we are encountering in this Unit section by the direct application of Ohm's law and common sense.

Example (7). A meter has a f.s.d. of 0.5 mA and a resistance of 1000 Ω. It is used as a voltmeter by the addition of a series resistor and is scaled 0–10 V. Design a suitable protection circuit using a 7 V Zener diode so that the instrument will not be overloaded by connection to voltage sources greater than 10 V.

There are two parts to this problem: we first have to find the value of the series resistor which converts the 0.5 mA f.s.d. meter into a 0–10 V voltmeter. Look at *Figure 3.17(a)*; when 10 V is applied to the circuit, 0.5. mA must flow through the meter. So

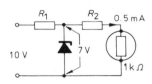

Figure 3.17(a)

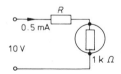

Figure 3.17(b)

$$R + 1000 = \frac{10}{0.5 \times 10^{-3}} = 20\,000\,\Omega$$

$$\therefore R = 19\,000\,\Omega$$

Figure 3.17(b) shows the protection circuit, and here $R_1 + R_2$ must be equal to 19 000 Ω. When the applied voltage is 10 V, the Zener must just break down, but the current through it will be negligible. At this time the meter must indicate f.s.d. The current through R_1, R_2 and the meter in series is therefore 0.5 mA. The situation, in other words, is identical with the circuit at (*a*). Then, for 7 V across the Zener

$$R_1 = \frac{10 - 7}{0.5 \times 10^{-3}} = 6000\,\Omega$$

and so $R_2 = 19\,000 - 6000 = 13\,000\,\Omega$

THE VARACTOR DIODE

An increasingly common application of semiconductor diodes is as variable capacitors. Such *varactors* depend for their action upon the depletion layer which forms at the *p-n* junction when zero or reverse bias is applied. As we have already noted, the depletion layer, being an intrinsic region free from charge carriers, acts as an insulator interposed between the *p*- and *n*-type regions. The width of the layer is a function of the applied reverse voltage. Under these conditions the diode acts as a parallel-plate capacitor, the junction contact area and the thickness of the dielectric (the depletion layer) determining the actual capacitance obtained. By variation of the reverse bias, the effective thickness of the dielectric is changed and so is the capacitance. *Figure 3.18* illustrates the principle.

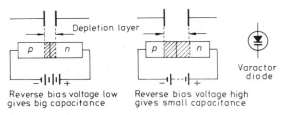

Reverse bias voltage low gives big capacitance   Reverse bias voltage high gives small capacitance

Figure 3.18

Typical capacitance variation is from 50 pF at 1 V reverse bias to 10 pF at 30 V reverse bias. Although the range of capacitance achieved may seem relatively small, these devices have many applications, particularly as tuning elements in such units as television tuners, and as control capacitors in automatic frequency control circuits. Their advantage is their small physical size together with the absence of any mechanical moving parts, the control of capacity being purely the control of a d.c. voltage applied as reverse bias.

PROBLEMS FOR SECTION 3

(8) Complete the following:

(a) An ideal diode has . . . . . forward resistance and . . . . . . reverse resistance.

(b) The power dissipated in an ideal diode would be . . . . . .

(c) A thermionic diode should be operated in the . . . . limited region only.

(d) In the circuit of *Figure 3.4* the average output voltage is . . . . . . V, where V is the r.m.s. secondary voltage.

(e) The addition of a reservoir capacitor to the output of a rectifier circuit . . . . . . the average output voltage and . . . . the ripple.

(f) In a two-diode full-wave rectifier circuit, the peak inverse voltage is . . . . the peak input voltage.

(9) A transformer feeding a bridge rectifier has a secondary voltage of 20 V r.m.s. What is the peak inverse voltage across the diodes?

(10) To avoid excessive bit wear when not in immediate use, 240 V mains voltage is applied to a 60 W soldering iron by way of a diode rectifier. Calculate, for this condition: (a) the r.m.s. current flowing, (b) the power dissipated in the iron, (c) the peak current.

(11) A rectifier diode has a constant forward resistance of 5 Ω and a reverse resistance which may be considered infinite. For a 100 V peak input and a 200 Ω load resistor, calculate: (a) the average current flowing, (b) the average voltage across the load, (c) the average voltage across the diode.

(12) What will be the peak voltage across the diode of Problem (11) (a) when it is conducting, (b) when it is not conducting?

(13) Refer to the half-wave rectifier circuit of *Figure 3.4*. What would be the effect on the output waveform shown if a resistor of value equal to R_L was connected (a) in series with the diode, (b) in parallel with the diode?

(14) A sinusoidal voltage $v = 50 \sin 314.2t$ is applied to a circuit made up of an ideal rectifier in series with a 20 Ω resistor. Sketch the current waveform in the resistor over a complete input cycle, carefully indicating the scale values. What is (a) the r.m.s. value of the supply voltage, (b) the r.m.s. value of the rectified current?

(15) The anode of a thermionic diode is at a voltage of 250 V d.c. and the current flowing through the valve is 20 mA. What power is being dissipated at the anode of the valve?

In the following five problems, refer to the circuit of *Figure 3.14*.

(16) Show that the power dissipated in the Zener diode is $(I_s - I_L). I_L R_L$.

(17) A 20 V stabilised supply is required from a 40 V d.c. input voltage V_s. A 20 V Zener diode is used having a power rating of 1 W. What value resistor is required for R_s?

(18) A Zener diode is to provide a 16 V stabilised output from a 20 V supply. The load resistor $R_L = 200 \Omega$ and the Zener current $I_z = 8$ mA. Find the value of the series resistor R_s and the power dissipated in it.

(19) If the Zener of Problem (17) stabilises down to a current of 0.5 mA calculate the greatest and least supply voltage V_s between which stabilisation will be obtained. Take $R_L = 2000 \Omega$.

(20) A 68 V, 3 W Zener diode is to be used to supply a variable load from a 100 V d.c. source. Find the value of the required series resistor if the Zener is not to be overloaded under any load conditions.

(21) A varactor diode has a relationship between applied voltage V and capacitance C (pF) given by $C = k/\sqrt{V}$ where k is a constant. If $C = 20$ pF when $V = 15$ V, what will be the capacitance when the voltage changes to 10 V?

4 The bipolar transistor

Aims: At the end of this Unit section you should be able to:
Understand the general structure of the bipolar transistor.
Identify the electrodes of a transistor as emitter, base and collector, and know the three modes of connection.
Define the current gains of a transistor connected in common-base and common-emitter mode, and state the relationship between these gains.
Sketch the static characteristics of common-base and common-emitter connected transistors.
Use characteristic curves for the evaluation of circuit impedances and gain.

The *bipolar transistor* is a semiconductor device which can act as an amplifier as well as a switch, which was the basic property of a diode. Because of its amplifying property it is also suited to perform as an oscillator. The transistor can therefore take over all the operations and applications which up to a few years ago were the sole province of the thermionic valve. It differs from the valve, however, in several important respects. In the valve, electrons are emitted from a heated cathode surface situated in an evacuated envelope, and their attraction to a nearby positively charged anode electrode constitutes the flow of current through the device. Control of this internal flow of electrons by means of a suitable electrode interposed between the cathode and anode surfaces leads to the property of voltage amplification. In the transistor, which is our main concern here, electrons (or holes) are injected into the solid material of the semiconductor and their subsequent movement through the body of the material constitutes the flow of current which can be similarly controlled. Operating voltages are considerably lower than those necessary for thermionic valves. Like the semiconductor diode, therefore, most transistors are small and compact elements, many times smaller than even the most miniature of valves.

THE JUNCTION TRANSISTOR

Consider a junction transistor as two junction diodes connected back to back, as illustrated in *Figure 4.1*. From either of these arrangements there are three external connections and these are known as the *emitter, base* and *collector* terminals of the transistor. Batteries are connected to the coupled diodes in such a way that the emitter-base diode is biased in the forward (low resistance) direction, and the base-collector diode is biased in the reverse (high resistance) direction. As the diagrams are drawn, diodes D_1 are conducting and diodes D_2 are switched off, in cases *(a)* and *(b)*. In both circuits there will be a small leakage current due to minority carriers moving across the reverse-biased base-collector diode junctions.

Now we shall not obtain the circuit properties of a transistor from two discrete diodes actually connected together in this way. In *Figure 4.1(a)* we have the arrangement *n-p-p-n*, and in *(b)* the arrangement *p-n-n-p* of the semiconductor material types. In both cases the centre portion is made up of two similar type materials, either two *p*-type

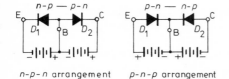

n-p-n arrangement   *p-n-p* arrangement

Figure 4.1(a)   **(b)**

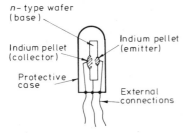

n-type wafer
(base)

Indium pellet
(collector)

Indium pellet
(emitter)

Protective
case

External
connections

Figure 4.2

anodes as at *(a)* or two *n*-type cathodes as at *(b)*. For transistor action, this centre base region must be a common interface between the outer emitter and collector electrodes. This is accomplished in manufacture by sandwiching a thin base wafer between two electrodes of opposite type material.

Figure 4.2 shows a cross section of a *p-n-p diffused junction transistor* made on the so-called alloying principle. During manufacture, the germanium or silicon is grown into a single crystal and doped with a suitable impurity, such as antimony, to make it *n*-type. It is then sawn and lapped to form a basic wafer whose thickness is of the order of 0.02 mm or less. Both surfaces of this wafer are then converted, to a carefully controlled depth, to *p*-type material by diffusing into them small pellets of indium placed on the surfaces. At a temperature of 155 °C the indium pellets melt and at 550 °C dissolve into the wafer to form a liquid alloy. On cooling, the alloy re-crystallises, leaving a small but sufficient amount of *p*-type impurity in the wafer material. Connecting leads are attached to the two indium pellets and to the wafer between them; the whole assembly, after suitable cleaning and etching treatment, is mounted in a small hermetically sealed container.

There are a great number of other manufacturing processes available which result in electrodes of different sizes and dispositions, but the basic action of the transistor is the same in each case; only such things as power handling capability and high frequency characteristics are affected by these different techniques of manufacture.

The *p-n-p* transistor, like the *n-p-n* transistor, is therefore a sandwich containing a *p-n* and an *n-p* junction connected in series, so that there is a common electrode of either *n*-type or *p*-type material (the base) at the centre of the sandwich. A pictorial representation and the circuit symbols for both types of transistor are shown in *Figure 4.3*, where the arrowhead on the emitter indicates in both cases the conventional direction of current flow in that part of the circuit. Conventional flow inside the transistor is therefore equivalent to the *direction of hole movement*.

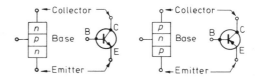

Figure 4.3

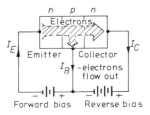

The indicated current direction
is the true electronic (electron)
flow. Conventional flow is in the
opposite direction

Figure 4.4

In *Figure 4.4* we have the representation of an *n-p-n* transistor with the appropriate forward and reverse biasing voltages applied to the respective parts of the circuits. The application of a negative potential to the emitter causes the electrons in the *n*-type material there to be repelled from the emitter region. The emitter therefore acts as a source of electrons and these flow into the base, which is biased positively with respect to the emitter. We have, in other words, a forward-biased diode. In the base region the electrons drift towards the collector by a process of diffusion and are accepted by the collector which is biased positively with respect to the base. Because the base is *p*-type, electrons exist there only as minority carriers, so the electrons arriving at the collector are derived almost entirely from the emitter supply. On their way across the base wafer, a small proportion (about 1–2%) of the electrons recombine with holes in the base region and this loss of charge is made good by a flow of base current. It is to reduce this 'loss' of electrons that the base is made very thin.

The effect seen from the external circuit is that of a fairly large flow of current (electrons) from emitter across the base to the collector, with a small flow of current from the base. For a small transistor, we might find such typical values as 1 mA for the emitter current I_E, 0.98 mA for the collector current I_C and the difference 0.02 mA base current I_B.

This is the mechanism of an *n-p-n* transistor. For a *p-n-p* device the majority carriers in the *p*-type emitter are holes. The emitter acts as a source of holes which flow into the base when the base is biased negatively with respect to the emitter. The collector is now biased negatively with respect to the base and so absorbs holes from the base region. Here a small proportion of the holes leaving the emitter recombine with electrons which are the majority carriers in the base, and this loss of charge is made good by a flow of electrons into the base as base current. (See *Figure 4.5.*) Compare the *p-n-p* figure with the *n-p-n* figure, noticing carefully the direction of movement of the electron or hole carriers inside the transistor and the corresponding movement of *electron carriers only* in the external circuit. You will probably find it easier to comprehend the *n-p-n* example at first, since the carriers in all parts of the circuit are electrons. Keep in mind that the *p-n-p* circuit simply reverses both battery connections and the external current directions. We will, in general, refer to *n-p-n* type transistors in the notes which follow.

Since the carriers originate at the emitter and distribute themselves between base and collector, the sum of the base and collector currents must always be equal to emitter current, so

$$I_E = I_C + I_B$$

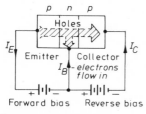

The indicated current direction is the true electronic (electron) flow. Conventional flow is in the opposite direction

Figure 4.5

CIRCUIT CONFIGURATIONS

There are three possible ways in which a transistor can be connected into a circuit, shown in *Figure 4.6* at (*a*), (*b*) and (*c*). In all cases one electrode is common to what we have called the input and output terminals, and the circuit configuration is described in terms of this common electrode. Hence (*a*) shows the *common-base* connection, (*b*) the *common-emitter* connection, and (*c*) the *common-collector* connection. The common electrode is usually treated as being at earth potential and the term 'earthed' or 'grounded' instead of 'common' is sometimes used to define the particular configuration; for example, (*a*) might be referred to as the 'grounded-base' connection.

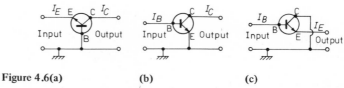

Figure 4.6(a)   **(b)**   **(c)**

Current Gain

Let us consider the relationship existing in each configuration between the input and output currents, assuming that we have battery supplies appropriately connected to the various terminals. We may define the ratio

$$\frac{\text{Current flowing in the output circuit}}{\text{Current flowing in the input circuit}}$$

as the static current gain of the transistor, the word static being used to imply that we are operating our devices solely from direct durrent sources, i.e. batteries, no other external components being involved.

Current gain in the common-base configuration is designated a_B* and is the ratio of collector current I_C to emitter current I_E. So

$$a_B = \frac{\text{Collector current}}{\text{Emitter current}} = \frac{I_C}{I_E}$$

In common-emitter configuration, current gain is designated a_E and is the ratio of collector current I_C to base current I_B. So this time

$$a_E = \frac{\text{Collector current}}{\text{Base current}} = \frac{I_C}{I_B}$$

There is a relationship between a_B and a_E because for all configurations the equation $I_E = I_C + I_B$ must be true. From the above definitions

$$\frac{a_B}{a_E} = \frac{I_B}{I_E} = \frac{I_E - I_C}{I_E}$$

since $I_B = I_E - I_C$. Hence

$$\frac{a_B}{a_E} = 1 - \frac{I_C}{I_E} = 1 - a_B$$

So, rearranging:

$$a_E = \frac{a_B}{1 - a_B}$$

By transposition

$$a_B = \frac{a_E}{1 + a_E}$$

You should remember these two important basic relationships. Now try the following problems.

(1) An arrow on the emitter symbol that points towards the base indicates a (an) . . . . transistor.

(2) The circuit configuration in which the input is between base and emitter and the output is between collector and emitter is the . . . . connection.

(3) An *n-p-n* transistor requires a . . . . collector operating voltage.

*The symbols h_{FE} and h_{FB} are commonly used for static current gain, but we shall retain the alternative symbols a_E and a_B in this book.

(4) A transistor has an emitter current of 2.5 mA and a collector current of 2.4 mA. What is its base current?

(5) For the transistor of the previous problem, calculate its current gain for (i) common-base, (ii) common-emitter connection.

(6) What current ratio defines the gain of the common-collector configuration? (Look at *Figure 4.6(c)* if you wish.) Prove that this current gain, a_C, is equivalent to $1 + a_E$.

You should have discovered one or two important facts from working these test problems, in conjunction with what has gone before. For one thing, the ratio

$$a_B = \frac{I_C}{I_E} \text{ is always less than 1}$$

for the reason that I_C is always less than I_E. In the same way, the ratio

$$a_E = \frac{I_C}{I_B} \text{ is always greater than 1}$$

for the reason that I_C is always greater than I_B.

Further, the current gain a_C of the common-collector configuration is clearly always greater than 1, since $a_C = 1 + a_E$.

Typical figures for the current gains of common-base and common-emitter connections are 0.97 to 0.998 and 30 to 500 respectively.

(7) A transistor has a common-emitter current gain of 100. What will be its gain in common-base?

(8) The common-base gain of a transistor is 0.985. What is its gain in common-emitter?

From the point of view of current gain, the common-base connection seems of no value as an amplifier, but it has other advantages which make it a relatively common configuration in practical electronic circuits.

CHARACTERISTIC CURVES

Because the transistor is a device having three terminals, there are a number of measurements which may be made on it in comparison with the simple relationship between current and voltage which is made on the semiconductor diode.

In the notes which follow the conventional procedure for identification of the various circuit voltages and currents will be followed. It is customary to fix the common rail (in most cases this is the earth or chassis line) at 0 V and to measure all voltages relative to this. So for an *n-p-n* transistor, voltages measured will be positive, and for a *p-n-p* transistor they will be negative. The exception is the voltage measured between emitter and base in common-base configuration when the base is connected directly to the zero rail. Voltages will be identified

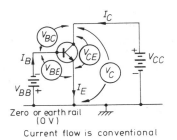

Figure 4.7

by two subscripts if they act between two definite terminals of the transistor, or if they are voltage sources such as battery supplies; and with a single subscript when they act relative to the zero rail. *Figure 4.7* shows this convention in use. V_C, for example, refers to the collector voltage relative to the zero rail, but V_{CE} refers to the voltage acting between collector and emitter. If the emitter is connected directly to the zero rail as shown in the figure, clearly V_C would be identical to V_{CE}, but would differ if, for instance, a resistor was connected in either the emitter or collector lead. Capital letters are used throughout and indicate that d.c. measurements are being considered.

There are four quantities, or *parameters* as they are called, which can be either held at a constant value or varied during the course of a measurement experiment, and these are: (a) input voltage, (b) input current, (c) output voltage and (d) output current. Four characteristic graphs may be drawn involving pair combinations of these so as to describe the d.c. performance of the transistor completely.

These *static characteristics* are usually found for particular transistors in the manufacturer's literature. The three most important characteristic curves for these two modes of connection will now be discussed.

The Input Characteristic   The input characteristic of a transistor is a plot of input current against input voltage, hence it concerns only the base-emitter junction which is the equivalent of a forward biased diode. For the common-base configuration, where the 'live' input terminal is the emitter and the base is at the zero rail potential, the emitter current I_E is measured for a range of values of base-emitter voltage V_{BE}, the collector being maintained throughout the measurement at a constant voltage V_{CB}.

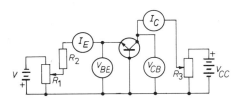

Figure 4.8(a)

Figure 4.8(a) shows a suitable circuit arrangement for such an experiment. V_{CB} is fixed by a suitable setting of R_3, usually to a value at which the transistor would be used in practice, and V_{BE} is varied in suitable steps by potentiometer R_1. R_2 is simply a safety resistor included to prevent excessive base current being drawn. Corresponding values of I_E are then recorded from the milliammeter wired in series with the emitter input. A graph of I_E against V_{BE} can then be plotted in the manner shown in *Figure 4.8(b)**. Notice that the value assigned to V_{CB} during the measurements is stated on the graph paper, in our case by way of example $V_{CB} = 6$ V.

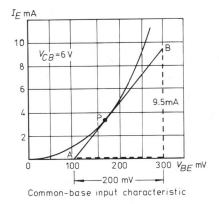

Common-base input characteristic

Figure 4.8(b)

*In all graphs, voltage and current axes will always be indicated positive, so that the first quadrant of the co-ordinate axes will contain the required curves. This is quite conventional, although strictly when negative values are involved, other quadrants should be used to give a true graphical representation. Some older books show such reversed axes. The shape of the curves and the deductions drawn from them are not affected in any way by the positive axes convention.

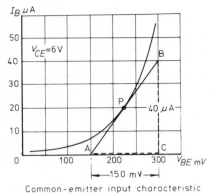

Common-emitter input characteristic

Figure 4.9(b)

For the common-emitter configuration, the 'live' input terminal is the base and the emitter is at the zero rail potential. Hence base current I_B is measured for a range of values of base-emitter voltage V_{BE}, the collector again being maintained at a constant voltage V_{CE}. A suitable circuit is illustrated in *Figure 4.9(a)*, and a typical graph resulting from such an experiment at (*b*).

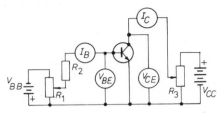

Figure 4.9(a)

What information do the input characteristics of transistors give us? One of the chief interests is the *input resistance* of the transistor — what magnitude of resistance would I 'see' if I looked into the input terminals of the transistor? This parameter is very important in the study and design of transistor amplifiers. One thing we can be fairly certain about — the input resistance is likely to be relatively low because we are looking into a forward biased diode. However, by the proper use of the input characteristic we can find out quite accurately what the actual working resistances for the two modes of connection will be.

Return to *Figure 4.8(b)*, the common-base input curve. The graph gives us related values of I_E and V_{BE}; we could therefore select any point on the curve, read off the pair of related values represented by the point, and by the division V_{BE}/I_E obtain the usual Ohm's law value of resistance at that point. However, the graph is markedly non-linear and we should clearly obtain a different value for the resistance at every point selected. We are more concerned with the ratio

$$\frac{\text{The small change in } V_{BE}}{\text{The small change in } I_E}$$

because when the transistor is used as an amplifier, the input signal is not a d.c. level but a small alternating quantity superimposed on a fixed d.c. level. The choice of the d.c. level depends upon the exact circuit requirements and once selected it is referred to as the d.c. operating point P. The above ratio is then found as the gradient of the curve at the point P. The value for input resistance we then obtain is called the *dynamic input resistance* of the transistor under actual signal conditions, unlike the static resistance found as the simple division V_{BE}/I_E. The dynamic input resistance is then

$$R_i = \frac{\text{The small change in } V_{BE}}{\text{The small change in } I_E} = \frac{dV_{BE}}{dI_E}{}^*$$

for a constant V_{CB}.

*This is the shorthand mathematical symbolism for the ratio. The d simply means 'a small change in ... ' For those who are not familiar with this symbolism and would like a further note on the subject of curve gradients, there is an Appendix on page 99 and it is strongly suggested that you read this before going any further in the text.

In *Figure 4.8(b)*, suppose the operating point P is at an emitter current of about 3.5 mA. Through this point a tangent AB is drawn; *the gradient of this tangent is the same as the gradient of the curve in the immediate neighbourhood of point P.* Now the ratio previously given is the ratio of the horizontal change in V_{BE}, the length AC, to the corresponding change in I_E, the length BC. Hence the changes considered are 200 mV in voltage for 9.5 mA in current. Therefore

$$R_i = \frac{AC}{BC} = \frac{200 \times 10^{-3}}{9.5 \times 10^{-3}}$$

$$= \frac{200}{9.5} = 21 \ \Omega$$

In *Figure 4.9(b)* we have the input characteristic in common-emitter mode. Since the vertical scale is now in microamperes, it is obvious that the input resistance will be much higher than in common-base mode. Taking a point P corresponding to a base current of 20 μA and drawing the tangent AB as before, it is seen that

$$R_i = \frac{AC}{BC} = \frac{150 \times 10^{-3}}{40 \times 10^{-6}}$$

$$= \frac{150 \times 10^3}{40} = 3750 \ \Omega$$

The values obtained for R_i for the common-base and the common-emitter modes are quite typical; actual values of course depend upon the transistor, the working voltages and selection of the operating point.

(9) Referring to *Figures 4.8(b)* and *4.9(b)*, estimate the dynamic input resistance for each mode of connection, assuming that the operating point P is at I_E = 2 mA for common-base, and at I_B = 10 μA for common-emitter. (Use a pencil to avoid spoiling your book diagrams.)

The Output Characteristic

The output characteristic is possibly the most useful of transistor characteristic curves because it not only enables us to find the *output resistance R_o* of the configuration but several other useful parameters may be derived from it.

The output characteristic is a plot of collector current I_C against collector voltage for fixed values of base current in common-emitter mode or emitter current in common-base mode. It is usual to draw a family of curves for each configuration over a range of fixed values for I_E or I_B. The circuit of *Figure 4.8(a)* can be used now to plot the output characteristic of the common-base mode. I_E is fixed at, say, 2 mA by suitable adjustment of potentiometer R_1, and V_{CB} is then varied in a series of voltage steps by R_3. Corresponding values of I_C are then recorded for each step in V_{CB} from the milliammeter wired in series with the collector lead. A graph of I_C against V_{CB} can then be plotted as shown in the lower curve of *Figure 4.10*. The experiment is repeated for other fixed values of I_E; in the figure these values are

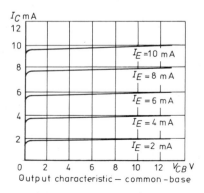

Output characteristic — common-base

Figure 4.10

taken to be in 2 mA intervals up to a maximum of 10 mA. In this way a family of curves is obtained which may, if necessary, be interpolated for estimation of collector voltage and current at other values of emitter current. Each curve is basically the same shape and the portions above a fraction of a volt of applied V_{CB} are practically horizontal. Notice that for each setting of I_E the collector current is almost identical to I_E, the small difference in each case being the base current.

(10) Referring to *Figure 4.10*, can you explain why collector current flows even when V_{CB} is zero?

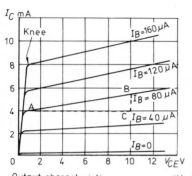

Figure 4.11

Output characteristic – common – emitter

For the common-emitter configuration, the circuit of *Figure 4.9(a)* may be used again. Since the base-collector junction is a reverse biased diode, a small leakage current will flow when $I_B = 0$. The lowest curve in *Figure 4.11* shows this effect; if the applied V_{CE} was increased sufficiently, the junction would break down at the avalanche (Zener) point. Now if by adjustment of potentiometer R_1 a small base current is set to flow, say, of 20 μA, and held constant while V_{CE} is adjusted throughout the available range of voltage, the next characteristic curve of the family is obtained. It is basically the same shape as before, reasonably flat, but not so flat as was the characteristic of the common-base mode, and the collector current is at a much higher level. For further settings of I_B, further curves are obtained. Again, when presented with such a family of output chracteristics we may interpolate to estimate collector current and voltage at other base current values from those shown.

Both sets of curves immediately tell us that the collector current which flows is substantially independent of collector voltage — the curves are practically horizontal lines. This is because collector current is derived from the charge carriers originating in the emitter. On entering the base under the emitter-base voltage these carriers are almost entirely gathered up by the collector, even if the collector-base voltage is very small. Increases in the collector voltage, therefore, have little effect on collector current because it is not the collector voltage which is producing the carriers. The horizontal portions of the curves represent *transistor saturation regions*. As far as the output terminals are concerned, the transistor behaves as a *constant current generator*, and this property has several useful applications in electronic circuit design.

Return now to *Figure 4.11*. The curves give us related values of I_C and V_{CE} for various values of I_B. The output resistance of the transistor is the effective resistance we should see by looking back into the output terminals; we should expect this to be relatively large because this time we are looking into a reverse biased diode. However, the value we measure is not simply the straightforward resistance of the collector-base diode junction. Working on the same principle as we did for the case of input resistance, we can say

$$R_o = \frac{\text{The small change in } V_{CE}}{\text{The small change in } I_C} = \frac{dV_{CE}}{dI_C}$$

and a triangle ABC drawn on the appropriate characteristic enables R_o to be evaluated. Strictly, the hypotenuse of the triangle, AB, is a tangent to the curve, but as the lines are for all practical purposes straight and parallel, the characteristic can be considered as the actual hypotenuse. What we are saying is that the gradient of the lines is constant. From the diagram then

$$R_o = \frac{AC}{BC} = \frac{9}{1.5 \times 10^{-3}} = 6000 \ \Omega \ (6 \ k\Omega)$$

Clearly, the output resistance increases as the characteristic lines become more horizontal, so referring to the curves for the common-base mode shown in *Figure 4.10*, it is apparent that the output resistance for this mode of connection will be very high. A typical value would be 500 kΩ. The common-emitter, on the other hand, would have a typical output resistance of 20 kΩ; the curves of *Figure 4.11* were deliberately drawn to illustrate the calculation for R_o, and the value of 6 kΩ derived above is, in general terms, rather low.

The Transfer Characteristic   The transfer characteristic is a plot of the relationship between output current I_C and input current I_E or I_B, depending upon the mode of connection, at a specified collector voltage. The characteristic can be plotted directly from related values measured from the experimental circuits of *Figures 4.8* or *4.9*, or may be graphically derived from the respective output characteristics already discussed.

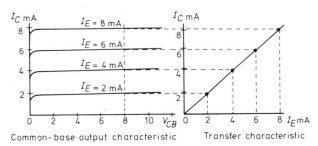

Figure 4.12

The output characteristics of *Figure 4.10* can be used to determine the common-base transfer characteristic in the manner shown in *Figure 4.12*. For a specified collector-base voltage V_{CB}, in this example taken to be 8 V, values of I_E are projected across to the co-ordinate axes shown on the right. Notice that the vertical axis of I_C is common to both graphs. Where these horizontal projections meet the verticals for corresponding values of I_E, points lying on the transfer characteristic are established. Joining these intersections gives us the required characteristic.

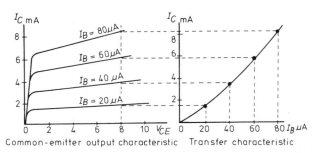

Figure 4.13

The common-emitter transfer characteristic can be obtained similarly from an output characteristic of the form of *Figure 4.11*, as shown in *Figure 4.13*. Here the specified collector-emitter voltage V_{CE} is again taken as 8 V. Values of I_B are projected across to the co-ordinate axes on the right of the figure, the vertical axis of I_C again being common to both graphs. Where these horizontal projections meet the verticals for corresponding values of I_B, points lying on the transfer characteristic are established, and the line joining them can be drawn in.

From the graphs, the gradients of the transfer characteristics give us

$$\frac{\mathrm{d}I_C}{\mathrm{d}I_E} = a_B ; \qquad \frac{\mathrm{d}I_C}{\mathrm{d}I_B} = a_E$$

the current gains in common-base and common-emitter mode respectively.

You will notice that the common-base transfer characteristic is much more linear than is the common-emitter. Since I_E is always $I_C + I_B$ and I_C is plotted against I_E in *Figure 4.12*, the line will have a gradient which is only slightly less than 45 °; a_B in other words is always slightly less than 1, since the tangent of 45 ° is 1.

(11) Use the transfer characteristic of *Figure 4.13* to obtain a rough estimation of the common-emitter current gain a_E.

Now work through the following test problems, making sure you are acquainted with the d.c. operating conditions of transistors in common-base and common-emitter modes of connection before going on to your study of transistor amplifiers in the next Unit section.

PROBLEMS FOR SECTION 4

(12) Complete the following statements:
(a) In normal operation the emitter-base diode is . . . . . . biased and the collector-base diode is . . . . . . biased.
(b) The carriers crossing the base of an *n-p-n* transistor are
. . . .
(c) A *p-n-p* transistor requires a . . . . collector operating voltage.
(d) The arrow on the emitter of an *n-p-n* transistor points . . . . . the base.
(e) The current gain of the . . . . mode is always less than unity.
(f) The input resistance of the common-base connection is much . . . . than is the input resistance of the common-emitter connection.
(g) $I_C + I_B$ is always equal to . . . .
(13) What are the values for a_E transistors having the following values of a_B (a) 0.980, (b) 0.975, (c) 0.970, (d) 0.96?
(14) Calculate a_B for transistors having the following values of a_E: (a) 50, (b) 75, (c) 110, (d) 350.
(15) A transistor has an emitter current of 1.5 mA and a base current of 10 μA. What will be its a_B and a_E values?

(16) Are the following statements true or false?

(a) In common-base mode: (i) I_E is dependent upon I_C; (ii) V_{EB} is dependent upon V_{CB}; (iii) I_C is independent of V_{CB}.

(b) In common-emitter mode, no collector current flows if the base is disconnected.

(c) Carriers injected by the emitter into the base region are of the same polarity as the collector.

(d) Collector voltage influences the number of carriers injected into the base by the emitter.

(17) If I_C = 4.0 mA when V_{CE} = 2.0 V, and 5.0 mA when 8.0 V, I_B being held constant, calculate the value of the output resistance under this condition.

(18) If I_C = 5.0 mA when V_{CB} = 8.0 V and 5.02 mA when 12 V, I_E being held constant, estimate a value for the output resistance of the transistor.

(19) In a common-emitter connected transistor, with V_{CE} held constant, a change of 80 mV in V_{BE} caused a change of 65 μA in I_B. What is the input resistance of the transistor under this condition?

(20) In a common-base transistor circuit, with V_{CB} held constant, V_{EB} is 120 mV when I_E is 1.0 mA, and 200 mV when 7.0 mA. What is the input resistance of the transistor?

(21) The table gives the input characteristic parameters of a small transistor in common-emitter mode, for V_{CE} = 4.5 V.

V_{BE}	75	100	125	150	175	200 (mV)
I_B	3	8	20	40	72	110 (μA)

Plot the input characteristic carefully, and from it evaluate the input resistance of the transistor when I_B = 40 μA.

(22) Describe an experiment to determine the input current/voltage, and the output current/voltage characteristics of a transistor connected in common-emitter configuration. Explain how the input and output resistances of the transistor can be deduced from these curves.

(23) The data given in the table refer to a transistor connected in common-emitter mode:

Collector volts, V_{CE}	Collector current, mA			
	Base current, 20 μA	Base current, 40 μA	Base current, 60 μA	Base current, 80 μA
3 V	0.91	1.60	2.30	3.0
5 V	0.93	1.70	2.50	3.25
7 V	0.97	1.85	2.70	3.55
9 V	0.99	2.04	3.0	4.05

Plot the output characteristics for base currents of 20, 40, 60 and 80 μA and use the curves to determine (a) the current gain a_E when the collector voltage is 6 V, (b) the output resistance when I_B = 60 μA.

5 The transistor as amplifier

Aims: At the end of this Unit section you should be able to:
Understand the operation of a small signal common-emitter amplifier.
Construct the load-line and determine the current and voltage gain
from the static characteristic curves.
Explain the necessity for base bias and its stabilisation.
Understand the significance of leakage current and describe thermal
runaway.
Calculate the voltage, current and power gains of the amplifier.

THE GENERAL AMPLIFIER

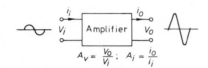

Figure 5.1

An amplifier is essentially a box having two input terminals and two output terminals, as shown in *Figure 5.1*. The box will contain one or more amplifying devices, transistors or valves, together with some associated components such as resistors and capacitors, and some kind of power supply derived from batteries or rectifier units of the kind described earlier.

We expect the amplifier to fulfil two conditions:

1. The output signal will be greater in amplitude than the input signal.

2. The output signal will be of exactly the same waveform (shape) as the input signal.

The first of these conditions is a measure of the voltage or current *amplification* or *gain* provided by the amplifier. We define

$$\text{Voltage amplification } A_v \;=\; \frac{\text{Output signal voltage } v_o}{\text{Input signal voltage } v_i}$$

and

$$\text{Current amplification } A_i \;=\; \frac{\text{Output signal current } i_o}{\text{Input signal current } i_i}$$

The signal voltages and currents will normally be measured in r.m.s. values, but for sinewave signals it is just as convenient in many cases to find the ratio of the input and output peak values; the resulting figures obtained for A_v and A_i are, of course, unaffected by this.

It is often necessary to know the power gain of an amplifier. This can be calculated from the product of voltage and current gains, so

$$A_p \;=\; \text{Voltage gain} \times \text{Current gain} \;=\; A_v . A_i$$

The second of the conditions means that the signal waveform should not suffer any *distortion* during the process of amplification. It is not a simple matter to design an amplifier having negligible distortion, at least not without sophisticated and expensive circuit systems. For simple amplifiers of the kind we shall be discussing in this section some

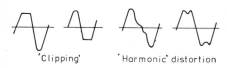

'Clipping'　　'Harmonic' distortion

Figure 5.2

distortion is inevitable, but it can be kept to a reasonably low level by careful attention to certain fundamental details.

Figure 5.2 shows some typical forms of distortion appearing at the output terminals of amplifiers, assuming a pure sinewave input. Some of the reasons for such distortion will become evident as we proceed.

Amplifiers can be classified into two main types:

1. *Small signal amplifiers*, which are designed to amplify small input signals, probably voltage levels of the order of a few microvolts to a few millivolts. An amplifier which immediately follows a record pick-up head or a microphone would be a small signal amplifier, as would an amplifier whose input was the very small radio-frequency signals received on an aerial. It is easier to avoid distortion in amplifiers of this kind than it is in the second category.

2. *Power amplifiers*. These have very large input signal voltages, of the order of several volts. Their output requirements are large current and voltage excursions so that considerable power is available for driving such devices as loudspeakers or, in industrial applications, small electric motors.

At this stage, we are interested only in small signal amplifiers dealing with relatively low frequency signals.

A single amplifier stage (one transistor or one valve) is rarely sufficient to supply the overall amplification needed. It is then necessary to use two or more devices in *cascade*, the output of one being fed into the input terminals of the next, and so on. The signal is then progressively amplified as it passes through the system. At the end, when a sufficient amplification (in the small signal sense) has been achieved, a power amplifier is introduced to provide the required final output level.

In this Unit section we shall investigate the amplifying properties of the transistor. As you have learned, a transistor consists of three layers of *n*- and *p*-type material; these layers form respectively the collector, base and emitter electrodes. The current flowing between the base and the collector can be controlled either by a current flowing in the emitter or in the base circuit, so the transistor is essentially a current operated device. A transistor is not capable on its own of providing amplification, but when it is employed in conjunction with an external *load resistor*, amplification becomes possible. The conventional amplifier arrangement thus consists of a source of power supply (batteries, etc.), a load, and the control device (transistor), connected in series as shown in *Figure 5.3*. The load does not have to be a resistor, it may take the form of a tuned circuit, for example, but for our immediate purposes we will present it as a resistor. From the diagram, the voltage amplification A_v is seen to be

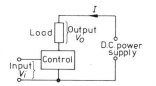

Figure 5.3

$$A_v = \frac{\text{Output signal voltage across the load}}{\text{Signal voltage present at the input}} = \frac{v_o}{v_i}$$

THE COMMON-EMITTER AMPLIFIER

For the two basic circuit configurations we discussed in the previous Unit section, we saw that the input resistance in both cases was the relatively low resistance of the forward-biased base-emitter junction; the output resistance was the relatively high resistance of the reverse-biased base-collector junction. It is this marked disparity between the input and output resistances, in conjunction with the external load resistor

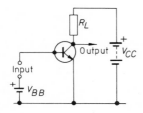

Figure 5.4

connected into the collector (output) circuit, which enables the transistor to act as an amplifier of alternating currents and voltages.

Figure 5.4 shows the basic circuit arrangement of a common-emitter amplifier. In the circuit, input takes place between base and emitter and the output is developed between collector and emitter. The emitter is the common electrode, and it is generally simpler to refer to the connection mode as base-input, collector-output amplification.

In the usual manner, the base is biased positively relative to the emitter (we are using an *n-p-n* transistor) by the battery V_{BB} and the collector is biased positively relative to the emitter (and the base) by battery V_{CC}. A load resistor R_L has been included in the collector lead. All this accords with what we have already discussed about basic transistor operation. The addition of R_L is the only major change in the general circuit arrangement. However, our previous work has dealt with the transistor only from the point of view of the d.c. battery conditions and on this basis (with no load resistor in circuit) we defined the static current gain

$$a_E = \frac{\text{Change in } I_C}{\text{Change in } I_B} \quad \text{with } V_{CE} \text{ constant}$$

On this basis also, we drew the various characteristic curves relating the various electrode voltages and currents.

We are concerned now with what happens when an alternating signal is applied to the input terminals; this is the signal that we require to amplify, be it speech, music or a simple single-frequency tone. For simplicity we shall consider the alternating input to be a single frequency sinewave, expressed in the customary way as $i = \hat{I}.\sin \omega t$. If the emitter-base voltage is allowed to alternate about a mean value, base current I_B also will vary about some mean value determined by battery V_{BB}. It is clear that the emitter current and hence the collector current will also vary about some mean value determined by V_{CC}. The load resistor R_L will have a p.d. developed across it by this alternating collector current, and this will represent the output alternating voltage from the amplifier. The processes involved are perhaps best brought out by way of a simple numerical example.

First, we recapitulate on the d.c. set up, assuming that the a.c. signal input is zero. *Figure 5.5(a)* shows the arrangement. As usual we have the base-emitter junction biased in the forward direction by V_{BB}. This bias is taken, purely as an illustrative example, to be 1 V. This then fixes what we shall call the *base-bias voltage*. Suppose that this bias causes a base current $I_B = 0.1$ mA to flow; then this value of base current determines the mean d.c. level of base current about which the a.c. input signal will swing alternately positive and negative. This is the *base current d.c. operating point*.

Now for this example the static current gain of the transistor, a_E, has been taken to be 50. Since 0.1 mA is the steady base current, the collector current I_C will be given by $I_C = a_E.I_B$, so

$$I_C = 50 \times 0.1 = 5 \text{ mA}$$

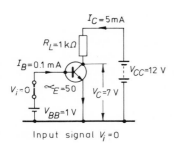

Figure 5.5(a)

This current is shown in the diagram. When 5 mA flows through the load R_L, taken here to be 1 kΩ, there will be a steady voltage drop across R_L given by $I_C.R_L = 5 \times 10^{-3} \times 1000 = 5$ V. The voltage at the collector V_{CE} will therefore be $V_{CC} - I_C R_L = 12 - 5 = 7$ V. This value of V_{CE} is the mean d.c. level about which the output a.c. voltage signal will swing alternately positive and negative. This is the *collector current d.c. operating point.* A transistor biased in this way is said to be operating in *Class A* conditions.

We have now fixed two quantities as operating points: the base current I_B at 0.1 mA, and the collector voltage V_{CE} at 7 V. This establishes the steady or static conditions. We now consider the *working* or *dynamic* conditions.

Turn to (b) of *Figure 5.5* and consider what happens when we apply the a.c. signal input in series with the base. The exact manner of doing this is unimportant at the moment. Suppose the input signal varies between the peak values +0.1 V and −0.1 V as shown, and imagine the condition at (b) to be such that the positive peak of the input is present at the input terminals. Then at this instant V_{BE} is increased by 0.1 V; suppose this causes I_B to increase by 0.05 mA, so that the instantaneous $I_B = 0.1 + 0.05$ mA $= 0.15$ mA. The collector current now increases to $0.15 \times 50 = 7.5$ mA and the voltage drop across R_L increases to $7.5 \times 10^{-3} \times 1000 = 7.5$ V. Hence the collector voltage V_{CE} *falls* to $12 - 7.5 = 5.5$ V. Notice now that for a change of 0.1 V at the base we have produced a change of 2.5 V across the collector load. If we consider the voltage across R_L as the output voltage, then

$$\text{Voltage gain} \ = \ \frac{\text{Voltage change across } R_L}{\text{Voltage change in } V_{EB}}$$

$$\therefore \ A_V \ = \ \frac{2.5}{0.1} \ = \ 25$$

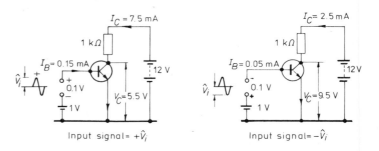

Figure 5.5(b)   (c)

The input signal now changes from its positive peak value through zero to its negative peak value. At the instant it passes through zero, the circuit conditions have returned to those shown in *Figure 5.5(a)* and I_B, I_C and V_{CE} are momentarily at their mean operating values of 0.1 mA, 5 mA and 7 V respectively. In (c) the input signal is at its most negative value, −0.1 V. At this instant V_{BE} is reduced by this amount and I_B decreases by 0.05 mA. The total I_B is now $0.1 - 0.05 = 0.05$ mA. The collector current correspondingly falls to $0.05 \times 50 = 2.5$ mA and the voltage drop across R_L becomes $2.5 \times 10^{-3} \times 1000 = 2.5$ V. Hence the collector voltage V_{CE} *rises* to $12 - 2.5 = 9.5$ V.

This cyclic variation of V_{CE} about its mean value of 7 V goes on all the time the input signal varies I_B about its mean value of 0.1 mA. The transistor then provides us with a voltage amplification of 25, and the output variation is an exact replica of the input variation, i.e. a sine-wave. Equal changes in I_B have caused equal changes in V_{CE}. There is therefore no distortion occurring in the process of amplification.

You will have noticed that we have interpreted the amplification provided by the transistor in the example as a voltage gain, symbolised A_V. There is also a current gain: I_B is changing by 0.05 mA on each input half-cycle and the output current is changing by 2.5 mA correspondingly, so we have a current gain of 50, or a_E. In an actual amplifier circuit, for reasons which we will not pursue here, the dynamic working gain is always *less* than the static value of a_E, but an appreciable current gain is, nevertheless, provided by the common-emitter amplifier.

(1) If the load resistor R_L is increased in value, there will be a greater voltage drop across it for a given collector current and hence a greater voltage gain. Is there any reason why R_L should not be made very large, say 1 MΩ, to obtain a large voltage gain?

We should note one other important point at this stage: when V_{BE} increased, V_{CE} decreased, and vice versa. The transistor therefore reverses the phase of the input voltage.

(2) Does the amplifier reverse the phase of the input current?

USING THE CHARACTERISTIC CURVES

To have a reasonably good idea of the way an actual transistor will work as an amplifier, we have to know a number of the quantities mentioned in the previous illustrative example fairly accurately: the exact point, for example, to which I_B should be set, what amplitude of input signal we expect, what collector supply voltage is available and which transistor we are going to use. All these things are inter-related and the choice of any one of them has to be made with an eye on the others.

Our starting point is the characteristic curves we discussed in the previous Unit section. We are considering the common-emitter amplifier here, so the static characteristics relating to the common-emitter configuration will be our concern.

We look first at the output characteristic curves, a set of which were given earlier in *Figure 4.11* and which are reproduced here as *Figure 5.6*

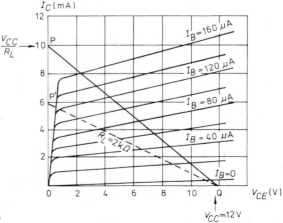

Figure 5.6

for easy reference. These curves relate collector current I_C to collector voltage V_{CE} for various fixed values of I_B. Now we cannot use these individual curves to solve our problems about amplification, because as soon as a sinusoidal signal is applied at the base terminal, I_B varies over a range of values as our earlier example showed, and the individual curves relate to a constant I_B. It is necessary first of all to draw across the characteristic curves another line, known as the *load line*, which will show us the relationship existing between I_C and V_{CE} when I_B is changing. To draw the load line it is necessary for us to know

1. The value of the collector load resistor R_L.
2. The collector supply voltage V_{CC}.

Of course, these values themselves also depend to a certain degree on other factors, but we have to make a start somewhere. Consider the circuit of *Figure 5.7*, where $R_L = 1.2$ kΩ and $V_{CC} = 12$ V. These are typical figures for a small amplifier stage. The collector voltage is given by

$$V_{CE} = V_{CC} - I_C R_L$$

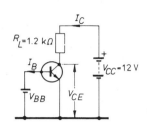

Figure 5.7

Now the supply voltage V_{CC} determines the value of the collector voltage when $I_C = 0$. Clearly, under this condition there is no voltage drop across R_L and so

$$V_{CE} = V_{CC}$$

This establishes the position of point Q on the characteristic curve V_{CE} axis in *Figure 5.6*, and obviously V_{CE} can never exceed this value. Since $V_{CC} = 12$ V, point Q represents this voltage limit.

Now suppose $V_{CE} = 0$. This can only happen if the voltage drop across R_L is exactly equal to V_{CC}. For the resistance given, 1.2 kΩ, and a voltage drop equal to 12 V, the collector current

$$I_C = \frac{V_{CC}}{R_L} = \frac{12}{1200} \text{ A} = 10 \text{ mA}$$

This condition establishes the position of point P on the I_C axis of the characteristic curves. By joining the points P and Q with a straight line we obtain the load line for the condition $R_L = 1.2$ kΩ.

For every given load resistance there will be a corresponding (and different) load line. If V_{CC} is kept at the same value, all the possible lines will start at the same point Q but will cut the I_C axis at different points P. Suppose, for example, R_L is increased to 2 kΩ. When the voltage dropped across this load is 12 V, the current flowing through it will be 12/2000 A = 6 mA, hence the load line for $R_L = 2$ kΩ will lie between Q and point P′ as shown in the broken line. It is evident that the gradient of the load line (its steepness) *decreases* as R_L *increases*, and vice versa.

(3) Using the curves of *Figure 5.6*, draw load lines (lightly in pencil) for the following conditions:

(a) $V_{CC} = 10$ V; $R_L = 1$ kΩ, $R_L = 2$ kΩ

(b) $V_{CC} = 8$ V; $R_L = 1$ kΩ, $R_L = 1.5$ kΩ

Now check your answers and rub out the lines!

(4) We have plotted load lines using two extreme points P and Q. How do we know that the lines connecting these are, in fact, *straight* lines?

So far, so good. We have seen how a load line can be drawn to suit a particular value of load resistor. We have now to see how a particular load line will help us in establishing the proper mean values of I_B and V_{CE} about which the input and output signal alternations will respectively swing. We have to find a value of I_B so that, when the signal is superimposed upon it, the current and voltage variations at the collector lie within the limits determined, and imposed, by the extremities of the load line. Quite plainly the collector voltage can never exceed V_{CC} (point Q on the line) and the collector current can never be greater than that value which would make V_{CE} zero (point P on the line).

In *Figure 5.8* we have taken the output characteristics for a transistor amplifier which is to be used with a 1.4 kΩ load and a V_{CC} of 14 V. The

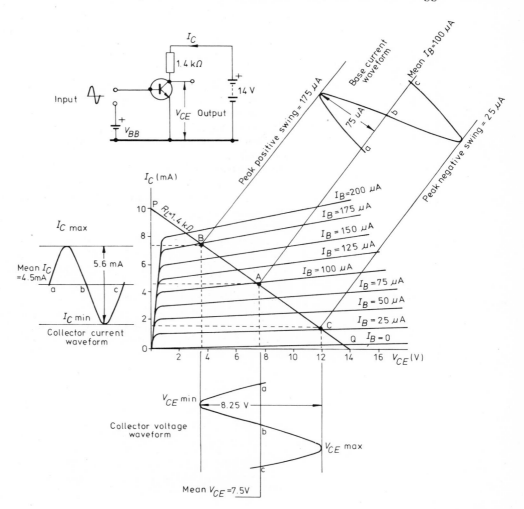

Figure 5.8

load line for $R_L = 1.4$ kΩ has been drawn in between points P and Q. The point A has been chosen as the base current operating point, i.e. $I_B = 100$ μA, because the excursions of I_B about this point which will result in proportional changes in I_C are very closely those between which the load line cuts through equal spacings between the static characteristics on either side of A. The distance from A to B and from A to C, in other words, represents the peak permissible swings of base current under the stipulation that AB is very closely equal to AC. Any appreciable swing beyond these limits will exaggerate the discrepancy between AB and AC, or, worse still, will carry the transistor beyond collector current cut-off at end Q or work into the curved portions of the characteristics at end P. If this is allowed to happen, the output signal will no longer be identical in shape with the base current variations and distortion will be present. It is not usually possible to get A exactly midway between the limits B and C, particularly if a very large input swing is to be handled, so a small amount of distortion is tolerated as the price for a large output signal.

The instantaneous values of the base current waveform are now projected on to the load line to give the corresponding values of I_C; the instantaneous values of I_C (i_C) are likewise projected on to the load line to give the corresponding values of instantaneous output voltage (v_o). Notice that the output voltage waveform is in antiphase with the input current waveform; when base current changes in a positive direction from 100 μA to 175 μA, the collector voltage changes in a negative direction from 7.5 V to about 3.7 V. As base current is in phase with base voltage, the output voltage is antiphase to the input voltage, as we deduced from our earlier example.

From the diagram the maximum excursions of base current for closely equal spacings in either direction about A, where $I_B = 100$ μA, is 75 μA. The corresponding excursions of I_C are about 2.8 mA about the mean value of 4.5 mA. The swing in V_{CE} is then about 4.15 V about the mean value of 7.5 V. These mean values of voltage and current are often referred to as the *quiescent values*, since they represent the no-signal operating conditions. As a rough and ready rule, a mean operating value for V_{CE} is taken to be $V_{CC}/2$ for the purpose of quick calculations.

The signal variations shown in *Figure 5.8* represent the maximum we can allow for this particular circuit if serious distortion is to be avoided. If you measure AB and AC, you will find them approximately equal. Of course, there is nothing to prevent us from making the input signal smaller so that the swing in I_B might be only from 100 μA at A down to 75 μA on one peak and up to 125 μA on the other. The equality of distance along the load line about A would then be almost ideal. What we should get would simply be a smaller output, but with reduced distortion. The operating point must therefore be chosen with care, and once chosen, *stabilised* against any effects which might tend to move it. We shall come to this problem in a very little while.

(5) What is the current gain, A_i, in the amplifier of *Figure 5.8*?
(6) Suppose the input current of this circuit flows in an input resistance of 1000 Ω. What is the approximate voltage gain, A_v?

LEAKAGE CURRENT

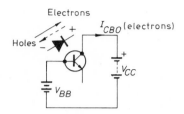

Figure 5.9

Before going any further into general amplifier theory, it is necessary to look into the problem of leakage current. Look at *Figure 5.9*, which shows an *n-p-n* transistor in common-base configuration but with its emitter lead disconnected. Under this condition it might appear that the collector current I_C would be zero, since clearly I_E is zero, but this is not so. The collector circuit is still connected through the reverse-biased base-collector diode, and this diode must pass reverse current. This is where some of the facts you learned in Unit section 2 should stand you in good stead. The leakage current is due to the movement of minority carriers (holes in the *n-p-n* transistor) across the junction, and its direction is opposite to that of the main forward current which would flow if the diode was forward-biased. But a movement of holes from collector to base inside the transistor is equivalent to a movement of electrons in the direction base-to-collector, hence in the external circuit the leakage current flows in the *same sense as that due to collected electrons*, the majority carriers. This leakage current is denoted by I_{CBO}, meaning that we are referring to the collector-base junction with O showing that the third electrode, the emitter, is left disconnected. This current still flows when the emitter is reconnected and the main forward current from the emitter is superimposed. So far we have taken the collector current to be $I_C = a_B I_E$. But with the addition of the leakage current, the true total collector current becomes $I_C = a_B I_E + I_{CBO}$, as *Figure 5.9* shows.

As I_{CBO} is very small at room temperatures (20–25 °C), particularly with silicon material, it might seem that the small addition to the normal relatively large forward current at the collector would be unimportant. This is true for the situation just described, but leakage current increases with increasing temperature and when we look at the problem in relation to the common-emitter configuration, such an increase leads to very undesirable effects in the transistor performance.

We illustrate the common-emitter situation in *Figure 5.10*. Here the base current is treated as the input. Since $I_E = I_C + I_B$ we can write the previous expression for I_C as

$$I_C = a_B(I_C + I_B) + I_{CBO}$$

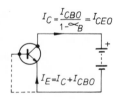

Figure 5.10

Then

$$I_C(1 - a_B) = a_B I_B + I_{CBO}$$

$$\therefore \quad I_C = \frac{a_B}{1 - a_B} I_B + \frac{1}{1 - a_B} \cdot I_{CBO}$$

Now

$$a_E = \frac{a_B}{1 - a_B}$$

$$\therefore \quad I_C = a_E I_B + \frac{I_{CBO}}{1 - a_B}$$

The first term here is the value of I_C we have so far taken as the output of the common-emitter amplifier with the input current equal to I_B. Refer back to page 34 if your memory has faded at this point. The second term must represent the *leakage current when the base is discon-nected*; this is denoted I_{CEO}. Hence

$$I_{CEO} = I_{CBO} \times \frac{1}{1 - a_B}$$

Hence, for common-emitter connection

$$\text{Total } I_C = a_E I_B + I_{CEO}$$

This is identical in form to the expression for I_C in common-base mode, but the values of the parts are quite different. Suppose, for example, that $a_B = 0.98$, so that $1/(1 - a_B) = 50$. Then I_{CEO} is 50 times as large as I_{CBO}, which clearly aggravates the problem we mentioned earlier about the increase in leakage current with rise in temperature. What is happening, in fact, is that in common-emitter mode, the transistor is amplifying its own leakage current! This is definitely a most undesirable state of affairs and a matter of serious concern in transistor applications. Try the next two problems to see if your ideas are straight about this leakage problem.

(7) If $I_C = 2.45$ mA, $I_{CBO} = 20$ μA and $I_E = 2.5$ mA, what is a_B?

(8) If I_B is zero for the above transistor, what is I_C?

SETTING THE OPERATING POINT

We return now to the topics we were discussing in relation to operation along the load line PQ of *Figure 5.8*. Having selected the operating bias point A on a particular load line drawn on a particular set of character-istics, it is necessary to set the bias current of the transistor concerned to the required value and ensure that it stays there. In *Figure 5.8* and in the earlier diagrams we assumed that a separate bias battery V_{BB} was used for this purpose, but in practical designs it is not convenient to have this arrangement and in general the base bias is obtained from the same source as the collector supply, that is, a single battery (V_{CC}) pro-vides all the necessary voltages throughout the amplifier. As the required bias voltage is much smaller than that required at the collector, the most simple modification is shown in *Figure 5.11*. Here the forward base bias is obtained by the insertion of a resistor R_B between the base and the positive terminal of the supply. The value of this resistor is easily calculated: in our example from *Figure 5.8*, the required I_B is 100 μA, hence

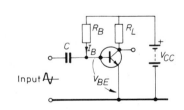

Figure 5.11

$$R_B = \frac{V_{CC}}{I_B} = \frac{14}{100 \times 10^{-6}} = 140 \text{ k}\Omega$$

This value actually includes the internal base-to-emitter resistance, but as this is of the order of some few hundred ohms, it may be ignored in the calculation. R_B consequently limits the base current in the forward direction to the required value, in this case 100 μA. It is important to notice, however, that the bias is not developed across R_B but across the base-emitter junction as the result of the no-signal (d.c.) current through that junction. This action makes the base positive with respect to the emitter, so biasing the diode in the forward direction.

(9) A transistor requires an operating base bias of 50 μA. The V_{CC} supply is 9 V. What value of resistor R_B is required to provide this bias?

(10) The above transistor has $a_E = 70$, and is used with a collector load R_L of 2000 Ω. What will be the steady voltage at the collector?

Now the use of a single biasing resistor like this is not particularly good practice from the point of view of maintaining stability in collector current. Suppose the temperature increases, then I_{CBO} also increases and I_{CEO} becomes a_E times this variation. Hence I_C increases, and V_{CE} and I_B are also influenced; for the d.c. collector current

$$I_C = a_E I_B + I_{CEO}$$

and the d.c. base current $= I_B - I_{CEO}$.

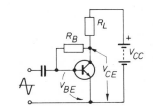

Figure 5.12

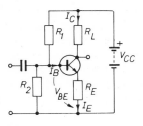

Figure 5.13

So, with any increase in leakage current, the total collector current increases and the total base current decreases. The operating point is consequently unstable, and the additional heating at the collector might lead to the effect of *thermal runaway* or at least to an increase in distortion. We shall discuss this in detail in a later note.

An alternative method of base biasing is shown in *Figure 5.12*. Here the resistor R_B is returned, not to the V_{CC} line, but to the collector itself. If now the collector current increases for any reason, the collector voltage V_{CE} will fall. As the base bias resistor is taken from the collector the base current will also fall, since $I_B = V_{CE}/R_B$. Hence the collector current $I_C = a_E I_B$ will also fall and tend to restore itself to its original (pre-rise) value.

Figure 5.13 shows the most commonly used bias arrangement. It consists of a potential divider circuit made up from resistors R_1 and R_2 connected in series across the supply, and an emitter resistor R_E. If the potential divider is made up so that the voltage level at the centre point (the base connection) is that required to establish the proper base current, but at the same time the total value of $R_1 + R_2$ is such that the current flowing through the divider is very large compared with I_B, then the base current will remain substantially constant regardless of variations in collector current. The emitter resistor in turn determines the value of emitter current which will flow for a given base voltage at the junction of R_1 and R_2. Any increase in I_C will produce an increase in I_E and this in turn will increase the voltage drop across R_E. This reduces the forward bias voltage V_{BE} which then leads to a reduction in I_C, so partly compensating for the original increase. This argument applies equally well to changes in collector current resulting either from changes in a_E (which happen when a transistor is changed) or in the supply voltage. Thus this circuit gives better d.c. operating stability than one in which the emitter is connected directly to the earth line. It is usual to make R_E of such a value that a drop of about 0.5–1 V occurs across it, and to proportion the divider so that R_2 is about 5 to 10 times the value of R_E. The total current through the divider should normally be at least ten times the mean value of base current.

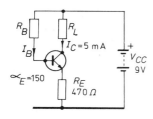

Figure 5.14

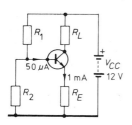

Figure 5.15

Example (11). A transistor with $a_E = 150$ is used in the circuit of *Figure 5.14*. The bias conditions are such that a collector current of 5 mA flows in the collector load. Ignoring leakage current and taking $V_{BE} = 0.65$ V, calculate a suitable value for R_B.

$$\text{Emitter current } I_E = \frac{I_C}{a_B} = \frac{a_E + 1}{a_E} \cdot I_C$$

$$= \frac{151}{150} \times 5 \times 10^{-3} = 5.033 \text{ mA}$$

$$\text{Emitter voltage} = I_E R_E = 5.033 \times 10^{-3} \times 470$$

$$= 2.366 \text{ V}$$

$$\therefore \quad \text{Base voltage} = 2.366 + 0.65$$

$$= 3.02 \text{ V}$$

$$\therefore \quad \text{Required voltage drop across } R_B = 9 - 3.02 = 5.98 \text{ V}$$

$$\text{Now} \quad \text{Base current } I_B = \frac{I_C}{a_E} = \frac{5 \times 10^{-3}}{150} = 33.3 \text{ } \mu\text{A}$$

$$\therefore \quad R_B = \frac{5.98}{33.3 \times 10^{-6}} = 180 \text{ k}\Omega$$

Example (12). Figure 5.15 shows a common-emitter amplifier with potential divider bias and an emitter resistor. The quiescent base current is 50 μA and the base-emitter voltage is 0.6 V. If the voltage drop across R_E is to be 1 V, assess suitable values for R_1, R_2, R_E and R_L.

For a 1 V drop across R_E at the indicated value of $I_E = 1$ mA $R_E = 1$ kΩ. The current through the divider has to be large relative to I_B, so taking the current in R_2 to be 10 I_B or 0.5 mA, the p.d. across $R_2 = V_{BE} + I_E R_E = 0.6 + 1.0 = 1.6$ V.

$$\therefore \quad R_2 = \frac{1.6}{0.5 \times 10^{-3}} = 3200 \text{ }\Omega$$

$$\text{Current in } R_1 = 11 I_B = 0.55 \text{ mA}$$

$$\therefore \quad \text{p.d. across } R_1 = V_{CC} - 1.6 = 10.4 \text{ V}$$

$$\therefore \quad R_1 = \frac{10.4}{0.55 \times 10^{-3}} = 19 \text{ k}\Omega$$

As there is a 1 V drop across R_E, 11 V is available for the drop across R_L and V_{CE} in series. It is reasonable to take the mean V_{CE} at about the midpoint of this supply, hence $V_{CE} = 5.5$ V. So, taking $I_E = I_C = 1$ mA

$$R_L = \frac{5.5}{10^{-3}} = 5500 \text{ }\Omega$$

THERMAL RUNAWAY

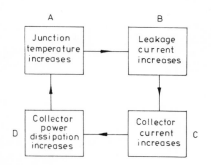

Figure 5.16

Thermal runaway is an effect which arises from the presence of leakage current in a transistor and can lead rapidly to the destruction of the transistor unless steps are taken to prevent its occurrence. Because of the amplifying effect on the leakage current in the common-emitter circuit, this mode of connection is much more susceptible to thermal runaway than is the common-base mode. We can best illustrate the effect by means of a closed loop diagram, *Figure 5.16*. Suppose there is an increase in the temperature of the base-collector junction — someone may have left his transistor radio receiver in bright sunlight or on top of a heated radiator! The increase in temperature shown at A then leads to an increase in leakage current as at B. This leakage current in turn leads to an increase in the total I_C, as at C, and this in itself raises the temperature of the junction by permitting more power to be dissipated at the collector, as at D. This brings us back to our starting point, so the initial temperature rise is augmented by the following train of events. This is known as a case of *positive feedback*; the events in the closed loop become self-sustaining and unless some action is taken to 'break' the chain at some point, the transistor current rises to such a high value that the base-collector diode avalanches out of control and the transistor is rapidly destroyed.

Apart from ensuring that the stability of the operating point is good, thermal runaway can be prevented by mounting the transistor on some form of heat sink which will conduct heat away from the junction as fast as it is produced. The important factor is the maximum junction temperature permissible before thermal agitation within the semiconductor material sets off the rise in leakage current which leads to thermal runaway. This maximum is about 85 °C for germanium and 150 °C for silicon, so germanium is most susceptible to temperature variations. For small transistors the junction is not normally in close thermal contact with the case. A simple form of heat sink can be used in such cases, taking the form of a clip-on corrugated aluminium tube or a copper 'flag' (*Figure 5.17*). These devices aid the loss of heat from the transistor case by increasing the contact area with the surrounding air.

Push-on corrugated heat sink   'Flag' heat sink   Power transistor

Figure 5.17

Power transistors are usually made so that the junction is in very close thermal contact with the case, the case itself being designed so that it can be bolted directly to a large metal surface. We have already mentioned this kind of cooling in connection with power rectifier diodes on page 22. *Figure 5.17* also shows a typical power transistor of this sort and the thick copper or aluminium base construction which forms an integral part of an external heat sink.

GAIN ESTIMATIONS

Although voltage and current gains can be estimated from the characteristic curves, it is sometimes sufficient to obtain values from simple formulae. The results are, of course, only approximations, but they are adequate for most general purposes. They are based on a knowledge of

R_L, R_i and a_E. Input resistance R_i can be deduced from the input characteristic for a given V_{CE} as explained on page 37.

Assume a collector signal current of i_c so that the signal voltage across R_L is $i_c R_L$. If the current gain is a_E, the base signal current $i_b = i_c/a_E$. Now for an input resistance R_i, the input voltage which must be applied across R_i to produce a base current of i_c/a_E is $i_c R_L/a_E$. Hence the voltage gain is given by the ratio

$$A_v = \frac{i_c R_L}{i_b R_i} = a_E \frac{R_L}{R_i}$$

The power gain of the amplifier can be evaluated similarly. The input signal power is given by $P_i = i_b{}^2 . R_i$ and the power delivered to the collector load by the transistor is $P_o = i_c{}^2 R_L$. Hence the power gain

$$A_p = \frac{P_o}{P_i} = \frac{i_c{}^2 . R_L}{i_b{}^2 . R_i} = a_E{}^2 \frac{R_L}{R_i}$$

$$= a_E \frac{v_o}{v_i}$$

A summary of the various gains for the common-emitter amplifier (and the common-base) follows, together with typical values of input and output resistance. You might care to try to verify some of these results for the common-base amplifier on the lines given for the common-emitter in this Unit section. You will find suitable common-base characteristics in the previous section.

	Common-emitter	Common-base
Input resistance, R_i	1 kΩ–3 kΩ	10 kΩ–500 kΩ
Output resistance, R_o	10 kΩ–50 kΩ	100 kΩ–1 MΩ
Current gain, A_i	High	Unity
Voltage gain, A_v	High	High
Power gain, A_p	High	Medium
Phase shift	180°	Zero

PROBLEMS FOR SECTION 5

All problems will relate to *n-p-n* common-emitter amplifiers, unless otherwise indicated or implied.

(13) Are the following statements true or false?

(a) Power gain may be expressed as $A_v{}^2/R_L$.

(b) If the junction temperature increases, V_{BE}, I_{CBO} and a_E all increase.

(c) If two transistor amplifiers each having a voltage gain of 10 are connected in cascade, the overall voltage gain is 20.

(d) I_{CBO} approximately doubles for every 10 °C rise in temperature.

(e) For a common-emitter amplifier, the change in I_C due to a change in I_B is $a_E \times$ change in I_B.

(f) If the load resistor is continually reduced in value, the gain of the amplifier continually approaches the value given by a_E.

(14) Plot the following characteristic curves:

V_{CE}	I_C (mA)			
	$I_B = 20\ \mu A$	$40\ \mu A$	$60\ \mu A$	$80\ \mu A$
3	0.91	1.60	2.30	3.00
5	0.93	1.70	2.50	3.25
7	0.97	1.85	2.70	3.55
9	1.00	2.05	3.00	4.05

The transistor concerned is used in a common-emitter amplifier with $R_L = 2500\ \Omega$ and $V_{CC} = 10$ V. Draw the load line for these conditions. From your diagram estimate (a) the value of I_B for $V_{CE} = 5$ V; (b) the current gain when $V_{CE} = 5.5$ V; the output voltage swing if I_B swings between 20 μA and 80 μA.

(15) A transistor is connected in common-emitter mode with $R_L = 12.5$ kΩ. The static current gain a_E is 100 and the input resistance is 1000 Ω. Find the voltage and power gains of the transistor.

(16) The data given in the following table refer to a transistor in common-emitter configuration. Plot the output characteristic curves.

V_{CE}	I_C (mA)		
	$I_B = 40\ \mu A$	$80\ \mu A$	$120\ \mu A$
2	2.2	4.4	6.4
4	2.4	4.8	7.0
6	2.6	5.2	7.6
8	2.8	5.6	8.2
10	3.0	6.0	8.8

Estimate (a) the output resistance of the transistor for $I_B = 80\ \mu$A; (b) the collector current when $I_B = 100\ \mu$A and $V_{CE} = 6$ V.

(17) The transistor of the previous problem is used as an amplifier with $V_{CC} = 12$ V and is biased to a base current of 80 μA. If the steady collector voltage V_{CE} is 6 V under this condition, estimate from the curves (a) the collector current, (b) the value of load resistor R_L.

(18) Refer to the curves you drew for Problem (14). Using the same load line conditions as before, determine the voltage gain, current gain and power gain when an input current of 30 μA peak varies sinusoidally about a mean value of 50 μA. You can take the input resistance as 1 kΩ.

(19) A circuit of the form shown in *Figure 5.14* has $a_E = 120$ and $V_{BE} = 0.7$ V. Estimate the values of collector load R_L and bias resistor R_B, if the mean (quiescent) collector current and voltage values are 9 mA and 4.5 V respectively.

(20) A circuit of the form shown in *Figure 5.15* has $V_{CC} = 12$ V, $I_C = 5$ mA, $a_E = 50$, $V_{CE} = 4$ V, $V_{BE} = 0.5$ V, and the voltage drop across R_E is 2 V. Find the values of R_L, R_E, R_1 and

D

R_2. (You may assume that the bleed current through the base potential divider is ten times I_B.)

(21) A common-emitter amplifier has R_L = 4.7 kΩ and is supplied from a battery V_{CC} = 15 V. If the collector current is 2 mA, what power is dissipated at the collector under quiescent conditions? What power is dissipated in the load resistor under the same conditions?

6 Oscillators

Aims: At the end of this Unit section you should be able to:
Understand the operation of an oscillator as an amplifier with positive feedback.
Describe an oscillator as made up of a frequency-determining network and an amplitude stabilising system.
Understand the function of an oscillatory L-C circuit and its application to a sinusoidal oscillator.
Sketch the circuit diagrams of tuned-collector and tuned-anode sinusoidal oscillators.
Describe methods of biasing and stabilisation in oscillators.
Describe a form of relaxation oscillator and waveforms other than sinusoidal.

In general, a voltage amplifier will convert a small a.c. input signal voltage into a large a.c. output signal voltage. Suppose a part of the output voltage is connected back into the input of the amplifier, then if certain conditions are satisfied the amplifier will be providing its own input. Any externally supplied input voltage may then be dispensed with and a *feedback loop* established within the amplifier system.

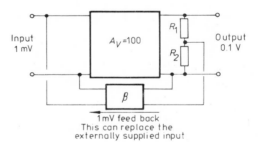

Figure 6.1

In *Figure 6.1*, suppose the amplifier has a voltage gain $A_v = 100$, so that for an input of 1 mV the output is 100 mV or 0.1 V. Suppose further that two resistors are connected in series across the output terminals so that $R_1 = 99R_2$; then for 0.1 V across the output terminals, the voltage across R_2 will be 1 mV. If this voltage is now connected back by way of a circuit network (whose exact form does not at present concern us) to the input, the process of amplification and feedback becomes self-sustaining and there will be a continuous signal output from the system. This output will be a steady alternating voltage, the frequency of which will depend upon the components used in the circuit. The production of such alternating voltages is one of great importance in electronics, and circuits which provide such outputs are known as *oscillators*.

Feedback taking place round an amplifier A and circuit network β forms what is known as a *positive feedback* loop. We have already encountered a feedback loop in our work on thermal runaway. There

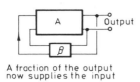

A fraction of the output
now supplies the input

Figure 6.2

the possibility of positive feedback was highly undesirable, but in oscillator systems it is an essential requirement.

There are two conditions which must be fulfilled for such an oscillator system to work and an output to be maintained, and we can consider these in relation to *Figure 6.2*:

1. The amplifier must be capable of supplying enough power to replace that which will be dissipated in the resistance of the feedback circuit loop and still supply sufficient power to its own input terminals to maintain the required level of output.

2. There must be zero or 360° phase shift round the complete loop so that the amplifier output signal is always in phase with the signal from the feedback circuit *β*. There are many mechanical analogies to this requirement. If a swing, for example, is to be maintained in continual and steady motion, then the pushes must be applied to it at just the right times — when the swing has reached the end of its travel one way and is just beginning to swing back. If we apply our pushes when the swing is still coming towards us, then it will not be long before the steady rhythm is disturbed and the motion might actually stop. So in the case of electrical oscillators, the signal fed back from the output must be precisely in step with the required signal at the input to keep the action maintained.

We can deduce from these two requirements that the amplifier circuit is that part of the feedback loop which maintains the amplitude of the output oscillation; and it is the *β* network which determines the frequency of the generated oscillation.

TYPES OF OSCILLATOR

Rectangular waves

Sawtooth waves

Figure 6.3

There are two basic types of oscillator:

1. Those in which the generated waveform is sinusoidal; these are *sinusoidal oscillators.*

2. Those in which the generated waveform is non-sinusoidal, i.e. rectangular or sawtooth waves such as those in *Figure 6.3*. Such oscillators are known as *relaxation oscillators.*

We have dealt with the simple amplifier in the previous section; our concern here will be with the *β* network circuit by way of which part of the amplifier output is fed back in correct phase and amplitude to the input of the amplifier.

(1) What are the two essential requirements for the production of steady oscillations?

(2) An oscillator producing a square wave output is known as a .... oscillator.

THE OSCILLATORY TUNED CIRCUIT

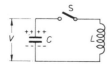

Figure 6.4(a)

In *Figure 6.4(a)* a charged capacitor *C* is connected by way of switch S to an inductor *L*. You will know from your work in Electrical Principles that if the capacitor is charged to a potential *V* volts and its capacitance is *C* farad, the energy stored in the electric field is $\frac{1}{2}CV^2$ J.

If switch S is now closed, the capacitor will discharge through the windings of *L* and a current will flow around the circuit in the direction indicated by *Figure 6.4(b)*. This current starts at zero and increases up to a maximum value. While it is rising, a magnetic field establishes itself

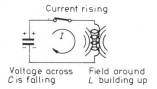

Figure 6.4(b)

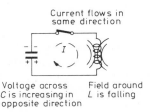

Figure 6.4(c)

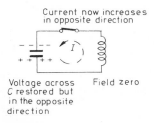

Figure 6.4(d)

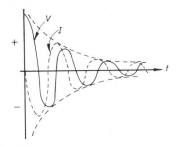

Figure 6.5

around the inductor and the voltage across the plates of the capacitor decreases. The current reaches its maximum value just as the capacitor voltage reaches zero, and at this instant the magnetic field surrounding the inductor is also at its maximum value. If the inductance of the inductor is L henries, the energy stored in the field is $\frac{1}{2}LI^2$ J. Hence (if we ignore the small resistive losses in the circuit where some of the energy is lost as heat), all the energy which was originally stored in the electric field of the capacitor has been transferred to the magnetic field of the inductor, so that $\frac{1}{2}CV^2 = \frac{1}{2}LI^2$.

Now with the capacitor voltage reduced to zero it might appear that the current would also fall immediately to zero, but as the magnetic field collapses an e.m.f. is induced in the inductor which acts in such a direction that it tends to oppose the fall in current — Lenz's law, remember? — and maintain its flow in the same direction as before (see *Figure 6.4(c)*). The capacitor consequently recharges towards the same potential as it had initially, but with opposite polarity. Finally, when the magnetic field has completely collapsed and the current is zero, all the energy stored in the magnetic field has been re-transferred to the electric field of the capacitor.

The cycle of events then repeats, the capacitor again discharging through the inductor and causing a current to build up in the opposite direction as in *Figure 6.4(d)*. This is an oscillatory action like the swing of a pendulum, and one cycle of the oscillation is completed when the capacitor is again recharged in the original direction.

If there were no resistive losses in the circuit, the transfer of energy from each component part to the other and back again would go on indefinitely and the voltage and current would vary sinusoidally at a constant amplitude. In a real circuit there are resistive and other forms of loss present and the amplitude of both the voltage and the current falls with each successive cycle of the oscillation. The oscillatory action is then referred to as a *damped* or *die-away* oscillation. This is illustrated in *Figure 6.5*. Obviously, to keep the oscillation going at a constant amplitude it is necessary to replace the energy lost over each complete cycle from an external source, and this can be achieved by the introduction of an amplifier. The oscillatory circuit, therefore, can be used as the frequency discriminating β network of a feedback system in conjunction with the amplitude determining amplifier A.

OSCILLATION FREQUENCY

By eliminating the effect of resistance, the L-C circuit will oscillate at a steady amplitude and at a steady frequency which will depend only upon the values assigned to the capacitor and the inductor.

Now if $\qquad \frac{1}{2}CV^2 = \frac{1}{2}LI^2$

then $\qquad V\sqrt{C} = I\sqrt{L}$

For an initial voltage V across C, the capacitor will discharge more quickly if L (and hence $\sqrt{L}$) is of small inductance, since the opposition to the build-up of current will be less. The time taken to discharge C completely is equal to one quarter-cycle of the generated wave and so is proportional to the time of one cycle, the periodic time. Since the periodic time $T = 1$/frequency, then the frequency of the oscillation is inversely proportional to $\sqrt{L}$.

Similarly for a given value of L, the smaller the value of C the less time it takes to discharge and the frequency is therefore also inversely proportional to $\sqrt{C}$. Hence

$$f \text{ is proportional to } \frac{1}{\sqrt{(LC)}}$$

or

$$f = k \cdot \frac{1}{\sqrt{(LC)}}$$

where k is a constant. You will recall from your work on Electrical Principles where the resonant circuit was discussed, that the frequency of resonance of an L-C circuit was

$$f_o = \frac{1}{2\pi\sqrt{(LC)}} \text{ Hz}$$

where L is the inductance in henries, C the capacitance in farads. This is also the frequency of the oscillatory circuit previously described, provided the resistance present is very small.

Hence by the correct choice of L and C, the circuit can be made oscillatory at any desired frequency.

> (3) What do you notice about the phase relationship between V and I in the oscillatory circuit?
> (4) An oscillatory circuit has $L = 100$ mH and $C = 0.01$ μF. What is the frequency of the oscillation generated?

THE L-C OSCILLATOR   The voltage sinewave produced by an oscillatory circuit will not die away but will be maintained at a constant amplitude if energy is supplied to the circuit to replace that dissipated in the resistive elements. This can be done by making the L-C circuit part of the feedback loop between the output and the input of an amplifier, as shown in *Figure 6.6*. This diagram is, of course, simply a pictorial representation. Notice that the oscillatory circuit takes the place of the β network in the general scheme. The two essential conditions mentioned earlier must now be satisfied:

1. The amplifier must have sufficient gain to replace the power dissipated in the circuit.

2. The output from the amplifier must be in phase with the signal set up by the oscillatory circuit so that the amplifier output assists the alternating current in this circuit.

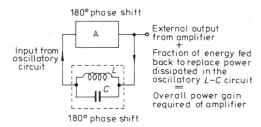

Figure 6.6

When the amplifier exactly replaces the power lost in the circuit, the loop gain around the complete circuit will be 1. If it is less than 1, the circuit will stop oscillating; if it is greater than 1, the circuit will oscillate and the oscillations will build up in amplitude until they are limited in some way. It is general to arrange the circuit feedback so that the loop gain is greater than 1, though not necessarily much greater. This ensures that the circuit will commence oscillating without difficulty. The build-up of amplitude which then follows is restricted by certain circuit conditions and the system stabilises itself at a loop gain which is equal to 1.

We will now examine some basic practical oscillator circuits.

COMMON-EMITTER OSCILLATORS

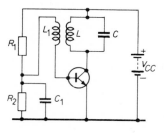

Figure 6.7

Figure 6.7 shows the basic circuit of a common-emitter amplifier having an oscillatory circuit wired into its collector circuit. For this reason this kind of oscillator is known as the *tuned-collector oscillator*.

Looking at the amplifier itself, you will recognise the conventional common-emitter configuration discussed in the previous section. Resistors R_1 and R_2 form a potential divider so that there is a constant d.c. voltage at the base of the transistor which biases it to the correct working point on the characteristic. The capacitor C_1 simply by-passes R_2 at the frequency of oscillation so that as far as the a.c. signal is concerned the junction of R_1 and R_2 is effectively short-circuited by the low reactance of C_1.

The oscillatory circuit L-C represents the feedback element connecting the amplifier output at the collector to the input at the base. Notice that this circuit now takes the place of the customary collector load resistor previously studied. The oscillatory voltage generated in the L-C circuit is coupled back to the base input by means of a coupling (or tertiary) winding L_1 which is a small coil wound in proximity to the main inductor L. This arrangement forms a transformer so that any change in the current flowing in L influences the magnetic field set up around L and causes an e.m.f. to be induced in L_1 in accordance with Faraday's law of induction. Clearly, the amount of energy fed back can be controlled by alteration of the coupling between L and L_1, i.e. the spacing of these coils can be modified until the required condition for proper circuit performance is established. A phase shift of zero or 360° is now required around the loop.

A transistor in common-emitter connection introduces a 180° phase shift as we have already seen; to obtain a total shift of 360° round the loop, the transformer must be connected so that it also introduces a 180° phase shift. This is easily arranged: by reversing the connections to one or other of its windings, the transformer will give an output that is either in phase or 180° out of phase (antiphase) with its input.

What happens in the circuit is fundamentally as follows: on switching on the d.c. (V_{CC}) supply, collector current commences to build up. This sets up a changing magnetic field in L and the resulting flux links with the neighbouring turns of L_1 so that an e.m.f. is induced in the base circuit. This e.m.f. will develop between base and emitter as an input voltage v_i and if this is in the proper phase it will augment the collector current flow. Once established in this way the L-C circuit will set up an oscillation by the interchange of energy between its component parts, a fraction of this oscillatory energy will be fed back to the base circuit as input to the amplifier, and the energy dissipated during each cycle in the resistances of the circuit will be made good by the d.c. source feeding the oscillator. Hence the oscillator converts direct current to alternating current, an effect opposite to that of a.c. rectification.

A common-emitter oscillator set up in this way is operating under Class A conditions, that is, the bias voltage is selected so that the transistor will operate about a point A over the linear part of its characteristic. When the loop gain is greater than 1 the base input signal increases with increases in the flux in inductor L and the amplitude of the generated oscillations rises rapidly. Needless to say, this process cannot continue indefinitely and once the amplitude of the base current reaches a certain value the transistor collector current begins to swing into the non-linear parts of the characteristic. This has the effect of introducing distortion, since the peaks of I_C now become clipped as shown in *Figure 6.8*. This is a state of affairs we try to avoid in pure amplifiers

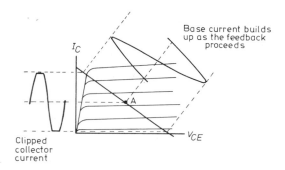

Figure 6.8

by keeping the base input at a low level. In the oscillator, however, there is nothing to prevent the base input building up in this way. Nevertheless, once the input swing cuts into the extremes of the characteristic curves, the gain of the transistor falls and the loop gain is reduced to 1. The amplitude of the oscillation then becomes constant. The distortion which is inevitably introduced can be kept small by ensuring that the loop gain with small signals is only a little above 1; this allows oscillation to commence but the excursions into the non-linear region are minimal. There are a number of techniques for achieving this end and it is not unusual to find several of these incorporated in one practical design. Two of these methods are described.

1. The number of turns on the coupling coil L_1 and its spacing from L are obviously adjustments which can be made during the course of design. Usually L_1 has fewer turns than L, often of the order of one-tenth or even less. The reduction in the coupling provides no compensation when the amount of feedback changes elsewhere in the circuit, for example, if a transistor is changed for one having a greater a_E (and a_E you will recall can have a wide spread in value), the feedback will be greater and the output may be seriously distorted. If the replacement has a lower a_E, the oscillation may stop entirely. In either case, the coupling would have to be readjusted, not necessarily a convenient procedure.

2. An emitter resistor (R_E) may be included in the emitter lead. Since $I_E \approx I_C$, the emitter current will be varying sinusoidally in phase

with I_C and an alternating voltage, which is proportional to the amplitude of the oscillation, will be developed across R_E. This voltage will be in opposition to the feedback signal generated between base and emitter (check this carefully for yourself), and will consequently tend to keep the amplitude constant. This arrangement compensates for variation in a_E between transistors to a marked degree.

The tuning of the oscillator can be carried out by varying either C or L in the oscillatory circuit. If the oscillator is going to be used at one single frequency it is usual to employ a fixed capacitor for C and adjust L by means of a dust-iron core, this core being sealed in position after the frequency has been set. For a variable frequency output it is more convenient to make C adjustable and a standard variable capacitor can be used for this purpose. In oscillators required to cover a wide range of frequency, the value of L may also be made variable by switching in different coils to the oscillatory circuit.

RELAXATION OSCILLATORS

Relaxation oscillators, as already mentioned, produce non-sinusoidal output waveforms. We will describe only one form of relaxation circuit here, the so-called free-running *multivibrator*. This is representative of relaxation oscillators in general and in fact forms the basis for several other varieties which have very many practical applications.

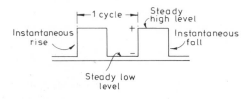

Figure 6.9(a)

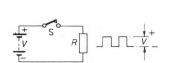

Figure 6.9(b)

The multivibrator produces a rectangular waveform of the form shown in *Figure 6.9(a)*, where the distinctive characteristics of a rectangular wave are indicated. Such a waveform can be produced by a simple switch and battery circuit as shown at (*b*). If the switch is opened and closed at regular intervals, the voltage output across R will be a rectangular wave. However, this method can hardly be used to generate rectangular waves at the rate of many tens of thousands per second or more, and an electronic circuit having transistors to perform the work of the switch is necessary. Such a circuit is a multivibrator; this circuit controls the time period that the rectangular waveform spends at both the high and low level states (these may or may not be equal) and so, in turn, determines the output frequency.

The circuit of a multivibrator is shown in *Figure 6.10*. You will see at once that the output of each transistor (at the collector) is fed back to the input (the base) of the other. This means that we have two common-emitter amplifiers each receiving its input from the other. This is clearly a case of a positive feedback loop, with the difference this time that the *whole* of the output of each transistor, not a fraction, is fed back as input to the other. Such feedback is said to be 100%. Also, since each transistor introduces a 180° voltage phase shift, the total loop shift will be the 360° required for oscillation to occur.

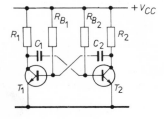

Figure 6.10

PROBLEMS FOR SECTION 6

(5) Complete the following statements:

(a) In a sinusoidal oscillator, the oscillatory L and C components determine the .... of the generated waveform.

(b) The amplifier is that part of a feedback loop which determines the .... of the output oscillation.

(c) A relaxation oscillator produces .... output waveforms.

(d) A free running multivibrator consists of two .... amplifiers with .... feedback.

(e) If the time constant of a multivibrator coupling components is doubled, the output frequency will be ....

(f) In *Figure 6.10*, when T_1 is conducting, its collector voltage will be at its .... value.

(g) In *Figure 6.10*, when transistor T_2 is conducting, the collector current of T_1 will be ....

(6) An oscillatory circuit, having $L = 100 \, \mu H$ is tuned with a capacitor which can be varied from 100 pF to 500 pF. What is the range of output frequencies obtainable from the circuit?

(7) In an oscillator L-C circuit, voltage and current are 90° out of phase. How do you reconcile this with the fact that if a tuned circuit is resonant, voltage and current are in phase?

(8) What is the time constant of a 1 μF capacitor connected in series with a 250 kΩ resistor?

(9) An amplifier with a voltage gain of 20 in the absence of feedback has 0.01 of its output voltage fed back in phase with the input, which is 1 mV. What is the voltage present at the input terminals? What is the overall voltage gain of the amplifier with feedback applied?

(10) There is no phase shift between input and output of a common-base transistor amplifier. Is it possible to use a transformer type feedback circuit with such an amplifier and obtain oscillations?

7 The cathode ray tube

Aims: At the end of this Unit section you should be able to:
Name the component parts of a cathode ray tube.
Explain the function of each component part.
Understand electrostatic and magnetic methods of beam deflection.
Discuss the factors affecting the deflection sensitivity.
Understand the principles of the simple time-base generator.

The cathode ray tube is a thermionic device designed for the special purpose of giving a visual representation, in the form of a graph, of a recurrent electrical quantity. It can be used to examine voltage and current waveforms, phase relationships and, with associated circuits, transient effects, response curves and device characteristics, to name only a few. In the entertainment field you will be familiar with it as the fundamental component part of a television receiver.

Cathode ray tubes are made up of three essential units:

1. An *electron 'gun'* which produces, from a heated cathode, an intense narrow beam of electrons moving at high velocity along the axis of the tube.

2. A *fluorescent screen* which produces a luminous spot when bombarded by the electron beam.

3. A *deflecting system* which enables the operator to shift the luminous spot to any part of the fluorescent screen area at will. This last unit may be internal or external to the tube proper.

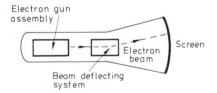

Electron gun
assembly

Electron
beam

Screen

Beam deflecting
system

Figure 7.1

The complete assembly of electron gun and deflecting system, when the latter is an internal part of the tube, is mounted in a glass bulb which is exhausted of air. The general arrangement is shown in *Figure 7.1*.

Tubes fall into two main categories: those types in which the deflection of the electron beam and also the focusing of it are brought about by electrostatic means, that is, by the application of suitable *voltages* to the component parts concerned; and those types in which these two functions are brought about by magnetic means, in general by the action of *currents* flowing through coils. Some tubes use a combination of both methods.

THE ELECTRON GUN

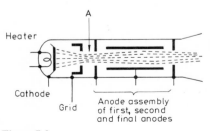

Heater

A

Cathode

Grid

Anode assembly
of first, second
and final anodes

Figure 7.2

The electron gun consists basically of three parts: a thermionic cathode emitter, an electron control component and an anode system which may or may not itself consist of more than one component. In the form of gun found in electrostatically controlled tubes, the anode assembly usually consists of three sections (*Figure 7.2*). Here the cathode (heated as in the case of thermionic valves by a separate filament) is surrounded by an inverted cup-like structure which has a small hole punched centrally in the end face. This structure is the 'grid' of the tube and it serves to control the forward movement of electrons emitted from the heated cathode. The anode system is made up of two or three disc or cylindrical electrodes, the first of these being mounted a short distance in front of the grid face and maintained in use at a fairly high positive potential with respect to the cathode. The grid on the other hand is normally maintained at a negative potential with respect to the cathode. Electrons emerging from the grid are accelerated forwards by the anode potential but at the same time they tend to bunch or constrict into a narrow waist at point A because of the repelling effect of the negative grid. Their own mutual repulsion, however, causes them to diverge again as they enter the second anode component.

It is during their passage through this second anode cylinder and their subsequent acceleration by the third (or final) anode disc that the electrons are brought to a sharply focused point on the fluorescent screen. All anode systems, whether of two or three sections, operate by virtue of the fact that the shape of the electric field established within them can be altered at will by adjustment of the voltages applied to the various parts. Any electron, finding itself in an electric field, will tend to move along the lines of force towards the positive potential, so for fields of the form shown for the two- and three-element anode systems in *Figure 7.3*, electrons which are not moving exactly along the axis of the system will be deflected towards the axis, and the beam will be brought to a sharp focus some distance ahead of the assembly. The amount of deflection in a three-element system is most markedly affected by the voltage applied to the second anode, and this electrode is normally taken to an adjustable voltage source so that control may be exercised over the focus condition. The customary method of obtaining the various electrode voltages from a single supply is illustrated in *Figure 7.4*. The voltages indicated and the component values are typical for a small cathode ray tube as used in a simple oscilloscope.

Notice particularly the method of maintaining the grid electrode negative with respect to the cathode. By making the grid sufficiently negative, all the emitted electrons are repelled and no spot is obtained at the screen. The grid control is therefore a control of the intensity of the spot, and is usually marked as a *brightness control*. The voltage on the final anode on the other hand determines the velocity of the electrons when they strike the screen. High velocity electrons will produce a brighter spot for a given density than will low velocity electrons. The requirements of an electron gun are consequently high beam density *and* high beam velocity, together with good focusing properties.

The electron gun in a magnetically focused tube is a much simpler assembly, consisting only of a cathode, a grid and a single accelerating anode. The focusing of the electron beam is accomplished by the use of a current-carrying coil or annular permanent magnet mounted on the outside of the glass neck of the tube. This magnetic assembly is in general very short compared with the length of the electron gun and is usually mounted a short distance ahead of the accelerating anode. The magnetic field is as shown in *Figure 7.5*, a longitudinal field parallel to the axis of the tube. Electrons moving along the axis of the tube are unaffected by the field, but any electron entering the field at an angle experiences a force tending to align it with the field, in exactly the same way that a current-carrying conductor (which is also a stream of electrons moving along a wire) experiences a force when the conductor is placed in a magnetic field. By adjustment either of the gap width for the case of a permanent magnet or of the current flowing in a coil in the case of an electromagnetic system, the electron beam can be brought to a sharp focus as it reaches the fluorescent screen.

The potential of the screen is usually held at that of the final anode

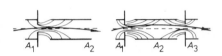

Figure 7.3

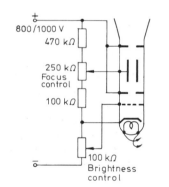

Figure 7.4

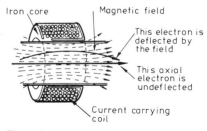

Figure 7.5

by being electrically connected to it through a graphite coating on the inner wall of the tube, and a return path for electrons reaching the screen is therefore provided. In the absence of such a return coating it would be possible for the screen to derive a large build-up of negative charge and so act to repel any further electrons. A large 'dead' spot would then be evident on the screen which would persist until the accumulated charge had been permitted to leak away. In the absence of a conducting path this might take a very long time.

THE DEFLECTING SYSTEM

In the absence of any further electrostatic or magnetic fields in the region between the final anode of the electron gun assembly and the screen, the electron beam will pass undeflected along the axis of the tube and strike the screen somewhere about its centre with the velocity it had on leaving the influence of the final anode. So that the spot produced on the screen may be moved to any part of the screen at will, it is necessary to be able to move the electron beam in both horizontal and vertical directions, simultaneously if required. This can be accomplished in practice in one of two ways:

1. By means of mutually perpendicular electric fields set up between pairs of parallel metal plates, which is *electrostatic deflection.*

2. By means of mutually perpendicular magnetic fields set up by currents flowing in pairs of externally mounted coils, which is *electromagnetic deflection.*

Two pairs of plates are required for the electrostatic method of deflection, and they are mounted inside the tube as shown in *Figure 7.6*. One pair controls the vertical movement of the beam, the other pair controls the horizontal movement of the beam. By adjustment of the plate polarity and of the potential applied between the plates, the electron beam can clearly be attracted to, or repelled from, a particular plate of a pair, hence can be moved to illuminate any desired part of the screen area. The plate pair controlling the vertical movement of the spot are called the *Y-plates*; the pair controlling the horizontal movement of the spot are called the *X-plates*. You should have no difficulty in remembering which is which if you recall the way you normally plot your mathematical graphs.

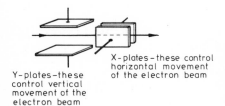

X-plates – these control horizontal movement of the electron beam

Y-plates – these control vertical movement of the electron beam

Figure 7.6

(1) Are the Y-plates mounted perpendicularly or horizontally in the tube?

As the plate pairs are set at different points along the tube axis to avoid any interaction between them, the pair of plates closer to the final anode will provide the greatest deflection at the screen for a given deflection voltage applied between the plates.

(2) Explain the reason for the statement which has just been made.

It is usual for the pair of plates closest to the final anode to be used as the Y-deflectors.

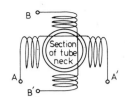

Coils A–A' connected in series
move the beam vertically. Coils
B–B' also in series move the
beam horizontally

Figure 7.7

Turning now to magnetically deflected tubes, two pairs of coils are positioned on the neck of the tube as shown in *Figure 7.7*. In practice the coils are folded saddle-fashion around the neck so that the field set up when a current is passed through the coils is substantially uniform across the tube section. You will see the best examples of magnetic deflection systems in television receivers, particularly some of the older models where the coil construction is relatively open to view. The deflection of the electron beam in the case of magnetic control is perpendicular to the direction of the axis of the pair of coils considered, i.e. the vertically mounted coils move the beam vertically, and conversely, for the other pair.

A major advantage of magnetic tubes over electrostatic types is that of greater structural simplicity, on account of the focus and deflecting systems being external to the tube, with the shorter overall tube length this makes possible. Electrostatic tubes, on the other hand, have none of the inductive effects present in coils which make the magnetic tube unresponsive to rapidly changing currents in its deflecting system.

DEFLECTION SENSITIVITY

It would seem reasonable to expect that we should be able to deflect the spot on the screen of an electrostatic tube as much as possible for the least possible voltage applied to the deflector plates. This condition means that we are looking for high *sensitivity of deflection*. Just as in the case, for example, of a sensitive moving-coil microammeter which gives us a large pointer movement for a small current in the coil, so a sensitive deflecting system in a cathode ray tube will move the spot an appreciable distance for only a small deflection voltage. We can define deflection sensitivity as the ratio (see *Figure 7.8*):

$$\frac{d}{V_D} = \frac{\text{Distance moved by spot across the screen}}{\text{Deflecting voltage applied}}$$

so that a measure of sensitivity will be the distance moved (usually given in mm) for unit potential difference (1 V) impressed across the plates. In some cases the ratio is inverted, and a manufacturer will express the deflection sensitivity of his tubes in volts per mm.

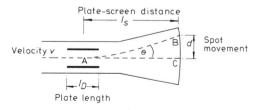

Figure 7.8

(3) When the voltage applied to the deflector plates of a certain tube changes by 50 V, the spot on the screen moves a distance of 18 mm. What is the deflection sensitivity of the plates?

What factors affect deflection sensitivity? In *Figure 7.8* we have noted the following factors:

(a) the length of the deflecting plates (l_D),
(b) the mean distance of the plates from the screen (l_s),
(c) the electron velocity (v).

All of these factors affect the deflection sensitivity, and their effects are interrelated.

First of all, for a given angle of deflection θ, it is clear from the diagram that the spot movement d will increase as the plate distance l_s increases. In turn, angle θ can be increased by increasing the plate length l_D, for the electrons then spend a longer time within the deflecting field and so suffer a greater deviation. However, the time spent by the electrons in passing through the field depends upon their velocity and this in turn is a function of the accelerating voltage applied to the final anode. If the velocity is high, as it has to be for good spot intensity, then the electrons are in the field for such a short time that the angle is small and so the sensitivity is low. It follows that spot brilliance can only be attained at the expense of deflection sensitivity.

Summing up all these conflicting factors, deflection sensitivity may be increased for a given electron velocity, i.e. for a given anode voltage, by

(a) lengthening the deflector plates,
(b) increasing the plate-to-screen distance.

The first of these methods can be used up to the point at which the beam would strike the positive plate before emerging from the field. It is usual to make the plates divergent for part of their length to avoid this, and *Figure 7.9* illustrates this point. It is not always practicable to increase the plate-to-screen distance for reasons of economy of space and good mechanical strength. The problem is overcome in more sophisticated systems by having the final accelerating voltage applied after deflection has occurred, known as the *post-deflection acceleration* (p.d.a.) method. The beam then traverses the deflector plate field at comparatively low velocity, hence permitting a large deflection angle to occur, but is accelerated after this so that spot intensity at the screen is high. The accelerating anode in such p.d.a. tubes is generally a graded graphite coating on the inner tube wall between the deflecting system and the screen.

Figure 7.9

Example (4). With the deflection sensitivity factors of the previous section in mind, deduce a mathematical equation for sensitivity in terms of plate length l_D, plate-screen separation l_s, and final anode voltage V_a.

Referring to the notes in question, we have these facts:

1. Sensitivity is *directly proportional* to plate-screen separation because, for example, *doubling* the distance AC in the triangle ABC in *Figure 7.8 doubles* the distance BC for a given angle θ.
2. Sensitivity is *inversely proportional* to the anode voltage V_a, because an *increase* in V_a increases the electron velocity which in turn *reduces* the angle θ for a given plate length l_D.
3. Sensitivity is *proportional* to the plate length l_D because, for example, *increasing* the plate length increases the time an

electron spends in the deflecting field and so *increases* the angle of deflection θ.

Writing sensitivity as the ratio d/V we can combine the above in the form of an equation:

$$\frac{d}{V_D} \text{ varies as } \frac{l_D \cdot l_s}{V_a}$$

Hence

$$\frac{d}{V_D} = k \cdot \frac{l_D \cdot l_s}{V_a} \text{ mm/V}$$

where k is a constant.

(5) In all the previous notes on sensitivity, we have assumed that the separation of the deflector plates themselves is fixed. Does the plate separation affect sensitivity, and if so, in what way?

THE SCREEN

The screen of a cathode ray tube is made as flat as possible consistent with the necessary mechanical strength, and is coated on the inside with one or more layers of chemical phosphor. Any substance which becomes luminous when bombarded by electrons is known as a phosphor, the kinetic energy given up by the electrons on impact appearing as light. There are two distinct effects involved: the light emitted during bombardment, known as *fluorescence*, and the light which continues to be emitted for a time after bombardment has ceased, known as *phosphorescence*. By the proper choice of screen material, the colour of the fluorescence can be made to suit almost any requirement, and the time taken for the phosphorescence to die away (the so-called 'afterglow' time) can be made to range from a few microseconds up to many minutes.

THE TIMEBASE

So far we have described a cathode ray tube in which we can focus a spot of light, control its brilliance and shift it about from one point to another on the screen. If we wish to observe a waveform on the screen we have to apply the principles we use when we are tracing an *x-y* graph on paper: it is necessary to cause the spot of light to traverse the screen in the horizontal plane at a steady velocity (so representing the *x*-axis of our graph), while at the same time deflecting the spot vertically to follow the variations in the waveform being observed (the *y*-axis variation). This is achieved by applying the waveform we wish to inspect to the Y-plates at the same time as applying a *sawtooth* waveform to the X-plates. This is a waveform we have already mentioned; when it is applied to the horizontal deflector plates of a cathode ray tube it is called a *timebase* or *sweep signal*.

Figure 7.10 shows the situation. The sawtooth wave, representing a linear rise in voltage, is applied to the X-plates so that the spot is moved uniformly across the screen. At the end of the rise, the voltage falls very rapidly to zero and the spot returns to its original position. As the sawtooth wave is repeated indefinitely, the effect of the spot movement is seen as that of a steady line traced across the screen, the afterglow of the fluorescent material and the natural persistence of vision of the eye

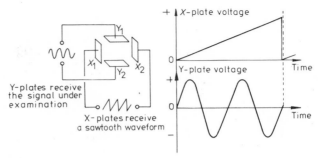

Figure 7.10

presenting the illusion of a straight line to what is actually a rapidly
repeated movement of a spot. If the frequency at which the horizontal
movement is repeated is known, then any simultaneous vertical deflection superimposed upon it by a signal on the Y-plates, will result in the
tracing of a graph representing the waveform of the applied vertical
variations over a period of time equal to the repetition rate of the horizontal movement. In the illustration it has been assumed that the period
of the sawtooth wave is one-half that of the sinusoidal wave which repres
ents the vertical deflection. Two complete cycles of the sinusoidal wave
are therefore displayed on the screen. It is normally necessary to ensure
that the frequency of the sawtooth is a submultiple of the frequency of
the observed waveform; if this is not so, then the trace on the screen
appears to move either towards the left or to the right and a proper
study of the waveform is difficult or impossible. By control of the sawtooth frequency, the frequencies can be synchronised so that a stationar
pattern is obtained on the screen.

The graphs traced in this manner are voltage-against-voltage curves,
since movement of the spot in either direction is achieved by voltage
variations applied to the appropriate deflector plates. If the horizontal
movement, however, varies in a known relationship to time (i.e. if the
sawtooth wave frequency and hence repetition period is known and
calibrated) the graph traced becomes effectively a voltage-against-time
curve. The base line is then a function of time, hence the name 'time-
bases' as applied to such special sweep voltages.

PROBLEMS FOR SECTION 7

(6) Complete the following:
    (a) The brightness of the trace depends upon electron . . . . .
and . . . .
    (b) If the screen glows for some time after electron
bombardment has ceased, the effect is called . . . .
    (c) If an electron moves left to right and a magnetic field is
directed into the page, the force acting on the electron acts . . . . .
the page.
    (d) Focusing is achieved in an electrostatic tube by an . . . .
field.
    (e) The Y-plates deflect the spot . . . .
    (f) Deflection sensitivity is measured in . . . .
(7) As applied to the formula given on page 72, a tube has
$l_D = 2.5$ cm, $l_s = 15$ cm, and $V_a = 800$ V. What is its deflection
sensitivity, given that the constant $k = 0.5$?

(8) A certain tube has a deflection sensitivity of 3 V/mm. What alteration in sensitivity will result from a 50% increase in the final anode voltage V_a?

(9) The time-base of an oscilloscope rises linearly in 12 ms. How many complete cycles of a 500 Hz sinewave would you see on the screen?

(10) A 2 kHz sinusoidal signal is being displayed on a cathode ray tube and five complete cycles are visible. In what time does the spot move across the tube screen?

(11) A cathode ray tube has equal X and Y sensitivities of 5 V/mm. A sinewave displayed on the tube has a peak-to-peak amplitude of 4 cm, and horizontally two full cycles occupy 5 cm. If the time-base voltage rises linearly at the rate of 100 V/ms, calculate (i) the r.m.s. voltage, (ii) the frequency of the waveform displayed.

8 Logic circuits

Aims: At the end of this Unit section you should be able to:
Understand the elementary rules of circuit logic and the construction of logical functions.
State the logical functions of AND, OR and NOT circuits.
Construct truth tables for AND, OR and NOT functions.
Recognise the Boolean symbols and the circuit symbols for AND, OR and NOT circuits.
Prove the equivalence of two logical expressions by the use of truth tables.

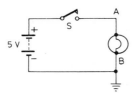

Figure 8.1

In the simple electrical circuit of *Figure 8.1* there are two possible states or conditions in which the circuit may be set: either switch S is closed and the lamp across terminals A and B is ON, or switch S is open and the lamp is OFF. This is an elementary *two-state* system. With such a system it is easily possible to transmit information from one place to another by using any prearranged code where the letters of the alphabet are represented by ordered arrangements of the ON and OFF states. Morse code itself is a two-state language, but here ON and OFF are replaced by SHORT and LONG; the signal pulses representing the letters are either dots or dashes or arrangements of these two possible duration states.

From a consideration of such elementary two-state ideas as these, it may seem a big step to computers and electronic control systems, but these also operate in two-state coding languages, and what appear to be extremely complex electronic devices are often actually complex only in the repetitive use of such basic circuits as that of *Figure 8.1* and one or two others we are going to meet on the following pages. In this section we shall be interested in what are called *logical circuits* and their associated so-called *logical equations*, circuits which operate in one or other of two possible conditions. Whether the conditions are simply referred to as ON and OFF, as in the lamp circuit, or as HIGH and LOW, UP and DOWN, PLUS and MINUS, TRUE and FALSE, to list only a few of the possibilities, is immaterial, but the number symbols 0 and 1 are probably best suited for our particular purpose and these are the symbols we shall normally use.

Logic itself, in its normally accepted sense, treats of the validity of thought and reason, truth and falsity being its two basic propositions. It may seem a far cry from a philosophy of this kind to the design of electronic circuits, but the complete symbolisation (putting into an algebraic form) of logic with its fundamental two-state foundations of truth and falsity has been made over the past hundred years, principally by the pioneering work of the mathematician George Boole (1815–1864), and applied to electronic systems in particular over the past 30 years or so.

Why are we particularly interested in two-state systems? Simply because so many electrical and magnetic devices have essentially two stable states, ON and OFF.

POSITIVE AND NEGATIVE LOGIC

There is one point to take care of before we go any further. Remember, we have decided on the use of the symbols 0 and 1 to represent each of two possible circuit states. However, if we simply leave things at that, an ambiguity is soon going to catch up with us. Go back to *Figure 8.1* and consider the voltage across the lamp terminals A and B, B being connected to earth, say. When the switch is open there will be 0 V at A with respect to earth and when the switch is closed there will be +5 V at A with respect to earth. The two possible states of the output therefore are 0 V and +5 V, each with respect to earth or terminal B. To which of these conditions shall we assign either our 0 or 1? It seems commonsense to assign 0 to the 0 V output state and 1 to the +5 V output state, but there is no reason why we should not choose the alternatives.

Suppose now the battery is reversed. This time the two outputs are going to be 0 V and −5 V with respect to earth. Again, we can choose 0 to represent the 0 V state and 1 to represent the −5 V state, but there is no reason why we should not choose the alternatives.

This sounds all very confusing, and as there are no definite rules about the problem it might seem that there are going to be difficulties ahead. However, we will apply the following conventions:

1. *Positive logic* labels the more positive voltage level as the logic state 1 and the other voltage level as the logic state 0.

2. *Negative logic* labels the more negative voltage level as the logic state 1 and the other voltage level as the logic state 0.

For most of our work in this Unit section we will operate in positive logic convention as conforming more to our 'commonsense' view of the two possible states of a system, that is, high level = 1, low level = 0.

RULES OF CIRCUIT LOGIC

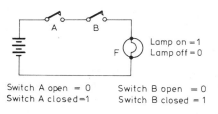

Switch A open = 0   Switch B open = 0
Switch A closed = 1   Switch B closed = 1

Figure 8.2

Simple switches provide us with a convenient starting point in the study of circuit logic because circuit devices such as relays, diodes and transistors can be switched on or off by simple circuit codes.

Figure 8.2 shows two switches connected in series with a battery (the signal) and a lamp (the output). We shall allocate the symbol 0 to represent an open (unoperated) switch and a 1 to represent a closed (operated) switch. Further, we shall represent an output voltage (lamp on) by 1 and no output voltage (lamp off) by 0. All these allocations conform to positive logic. Now suppose we wish to know the switch positions required if there is to be an output from the lamp. No problem here − obviously the lamp will light only if both switch A and switch B are closed. If either A or B or both are open (0), the output voltage will be 0. We accordingly call such a series circuit a *logical AND circuit*: there is an output (1) only if A = 1 and B = 1. Call the output F, then

$$A \text{ and } B = F$$

The symbol for AND is a dot (as used in the algebraic symbolism for multiplication), so we may write

$$A \cdot B = F$$

We can gather the information deduced from this circuit in the form of a table. This is called a *truth table*, and this is what it looks like:

Table 8.1

A	B	F	
0	0	0	→ A and B are off, no output
0	1	0	→ A is off and B is on, no output
1	0	0	→ A is on and B is off, no output
1	1	1	→ A is on and B is on, an output

Notice that there are four rows to the table. There are two switches each with two possible positions, so there are $2^2 = 4$ ways of arranging the switching. The notes on the right of the table show how the A and B rows are built up.

Check this table carefully to make certain you understand the way it has been set out: the A and B switch states have been put down in all four possible ways, and only if A and B are present together is there an output F.

We note: series connected switches represent logical AND functions.

Let the switches now be connected in parallel as shown in *Figure 8.3*. This time the lamp will light (1) if either A or B is closed (either = 1) or both A and B are closed (both = 1). If both A and B are open (0) the output F will be 0. As before there are four possible switch arrangements, but if either A = 1 or B = 1, or if A = B = 1, the circuit will be closed and the output will be 1. Such a parallel switch circuit represents a *logical OR circuit*.

The truth table for the logical OR function is as follows:

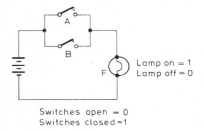

Lamp on = 1
Lamp off = 0

Switches open = 0
Switches closed = 1

Figure 8.3

Table 8.2

A	B	F
0	0	0
0	1	1
1	0	1
1	1	1

The A and B states have been set down in all four possible ways; only if A or B, or both A and B are present is there an output F, symbolised in the lower three rows of the table.

From the table, the logical equation can be deduced as

$$A \text{ or } B = F$$

The symbol for OR is v, although the symbol + (plus), now superseded, will be found in many books dealing with logic. Hence

$$A \vee B = F$$

(or A + B = F in the superseded symbolism).

We note: parallel connected switches represent logical OR functions.

Follow the next two worked examples carefully to familiarise yourself with these new and probably strange concepts.

Example (1). How many rows would there be in a truth table for a circuit containing *n* switches?

Since the variable quantities of logic have two states, or values, a certain number of binary variables taken together will produce a finite number of possible combinations. For example, if our variables are two switches each of which may be either ON or OFF, both switches taken together give four possible combinations: these we have seen in the earlier pages as OFF-OFF (0,0), OFF-ON (0,1), ON-OFF (1,0) and ON-ON (1,1). If we used three switches, each of which could be either ON or OFF, we would get eight possible combinations, for each of the above cases for two of the switches could be combined with the two positions for the third switch. Four switches would result in sixteen combinations and so on. The relationship is not difficult to spot as they go up in powers of 2: the number of possible combinations of the variables (switch positions) is 2^n where *n* is the number of switches.

Example (2). Draw circuit diagrams and draw up truth tables which represent the following logical equations:

(i) A.B.C = F;   (ii) A.(B v C) = F.

(i) This reads as 'A and B and C = F'. So there is an output F when A, B and C are simultaneously present. The circuit is clearly a series arrangement of three switches (*Figure 8.4*).

With three switches, each with two possible states, there are $2^3 = 8$ arrangements of the switch positions. Writing these in order under A, B and C headings gives the first three columns of the truth table (remember switch OFF = 0, switch ON = 1). The only condition for an output (1) at F is when switches A, B and C are all closed together. This corresponds to the last row in the table, so here F = 1. All other conditions for A, B and C give F = 0.

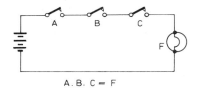

A.B.C = F

Figure 8.4

Table 8.3

A	B	C	F
0	0	0	0
0	0	1	0
0	1	0	0
0	1	1	0
1	0	0	0
1	0	1	0
1	1	0	0
1	1	1	1

(ii) This equation reads as 'A and (B or C) = F'. The circuit has to contain three switches A, B and C, and an output F will be obtained if A together with B or C are operated. The OR function represents a parallel arrangement of switches B and C, while the AND function puts switch A in series with them. The circuit is then assembled as shown in *Figure 8.5*. Satisfy yourself that this circuit will indeed perform the requirements stated in the given logical equation.

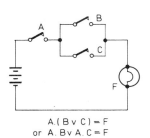

A.(B v C) = F
or A. B v A. C = F

Figure 8.5

For the truth table, there are once again three switches having eight possible contact arrangements, so the table has eight rows identical with those given in the previous example. An output F is only obtained, however, if at least A = 1, and either B or C or both B and C together are 1. The table follows:

Table 8.4

A	B	C	F
0	0	0	0
0	0	1	0
0	1	0	0
0	1	1	0
1	0	0	0
1	0	1	1
1	1	0	1
1	1	1	1

As A is 0 in the first four rows, F must also be 0, irrespective of what B and C happen to be. The fifth row has A = 1, but both B and C are 0, hence F is 0. Only the last three rows satisfy the condition of A present with B or C, or B and C together present at the same time.

Suppose we had 'multiplied out' the bracketed term in the equation of this example, just as though it had been an ordinary algebraic expression. We should have obtained.

$$A(B \vee C) = A.B \vee A.C = F$$

If you compare this alternative against the truth table, you will find that the conditions are satisfied, so the bit of algebraic manipulation seems justified: 'A and (B or C)' is exactly the same as A and B or A and C'. This is quite general: with a few exceptions which are peculiar to logic functions, all the ordinary rules of algebra can be applied.

Try the next problems yourself.

(3) Draw a circuit diagram and set up the truth table applicable to the logical function A v B v C = F.

(4) Represent the circuit shown in *Figure 8.6* in the form of a logical equation and a truth table.

(5) How many switching combinations are possible with the circuit of *Figure 8.7*? Write down a logical equation representing this circuit and draw up a truth table.

Figure 8.6

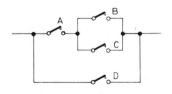

Figure 8.7

NEGATION

In logic, if one position of a two-position switch is A, the other position is not-A, symbolised as an A with a bar over it, $\overline{A}$. In a circuit we can represent negation by a switch that is normally closed as shown in *Figure 8.8*. In this case the unoperated switch represents the 0 condition, while operating the switch sets it to the 1 condition. Output voltage is present (F = 1) when the switch is normally closed (A = 0). The truth table for this circuit follows:

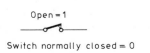

Open = 1

Switch normally closed = 0

Figure 8.8

Table 8.5

A	F
1	0
0	1

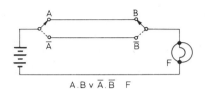

$$A.B \lor \overline{A}.\overline{B} = F$$

Figure 8.9

Example (6). A lamp is controlled by two change-over switches as shown in *Figure 8.9*. Set up the logical equation and truth table for this circuit and discuss the circuit operation in logic equation form.

Each switch has a position we shall call A and B respectively (shown in the full lines). When the switches are moved to their second positions, these become $\overline{A}$ and $\overline{B}$ respectively (broken lines). Again, there are four possible combinations of the switch positions.

Since there is an output (lamp on) for the positions A and B, and also for the positions $\overline{A}$ and $\overline{B}$, we can write

$$A.B = F \quad \text{or} \quad \overline{A}.\overline{B} = F$$

There is no possibility of a parallel connection, both switches must be in series for the light to operate. In other words, since the switches each have only two positions and both must be the same, there are only two possible paths for the lamp and battery to be connected: A.B is one and $\overline{A}.\overline{B}$ is the other. Hence, by combination, the lamp is on (F = 1) if A and B or not-A and not-B are actuated. Hence

$$A.B \lor \overline{A}.\overline{B} = F$$

which is the required logical equation.

The truth table is now easily deduced as follows:

Table 8.6

A	B	F	
1	1	1	⟶ A.B = F
1	0	0	
0	1	0	
0	0	1	⟶ $\overline{A}.\overline{B}$ = F

Example (7). Draw circuits representing the logical equations

$$\text{(i) } A.\overline{B} = F; \quad \text{(ii) } A.\overline{B} \lor \overline{A}.B = F.$$

(i) This equation asserts that there is an output F (1) whenever A and not-B ($\overline{B}$) are present together. Electrically, the equation can be represented simply by a series circuit containing a normally open switch A and a normally closed switch B, as shown in *Figure 8.10*. The circuit is completed (lamp on, F = 1) whenever switch A is placed in its closed position (1) and switch B is left in its normally closed position (0).

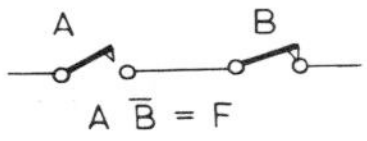

$$A\,\overline{B} = F$$

Figure 8.10

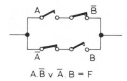

Figure 8.11

A.B̄ v Ā.B = F

(ii) This equation asserts that there is an output F whenever A and not-B or not-A and B are present. Electrically, the equation can be represented by two sets of series connected switches (A.B̄ and Ā.B), both sets being connected in parallel. The first set has B normally closed (for B̄) while the second set has A normally closed (for Ā). The circuit is shown in *Figure 8.11.*

LOGICAL RELATIONS

We can use the logical AND, OR and NOT (negation) definitions to establish certain logical relations. A logical equation is not simply the equivalent of an algebraic expression in the ordinary sense and results which may at first glance be taken as obvious (or otherwise), are not necessarily so. For easy reference, *Table 8.1* for logical AND is reproduced below:

A	B	A.B
0	0	0
0	1	0
1	0	0
1	1	1

replacing F by A.B, for convenience. Let A have its two possible values 0 and 1. When A = 0, the first row shows that 0.0 = 0. When A = 0 and B = 1, the second row shows that 0.1 = 0. Similarly, 1.0 = 0 and 1.1 = 1, as the remaining two rows indicate.

(8) Use reasoning to show that the following statements are true: A.Ā = 0, A.A = A, A.1 = A and sketch simple switching circuits to illustrate the statements.

By considering the truth table for the logical OR function (*Table 8.2*), you should now be able to deduce that 0 v 0 = 0, 0 v 1 = 1, 1 v 1 = 1 and A v Ā = 1.

Figure 8.12 summarises these rules of logical algebra in both table and circuit form.

Logic	Meaning	Circuit
0 . 0 = 0	Open in series with open is open	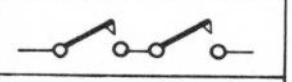
0 . 1 = 0	Open in series with closed is open	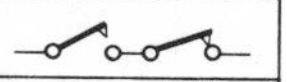
1 . 1 = 1	Closed in series with closed is closed	
A . Ā = 0	Switch in series with its negation is open	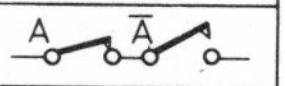
0 v 0 = 0	Open in parallel with open is open	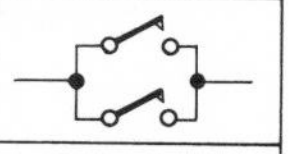
0 v 1 = 1	Open in parallel with closed is closed	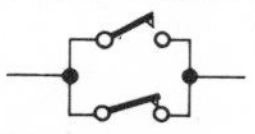
1 v 1 = 1	Closed in parallel with closed is closed	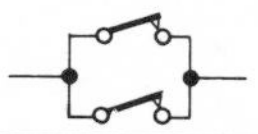
A v Ā = 1	Switch in parallel with its negation is closed	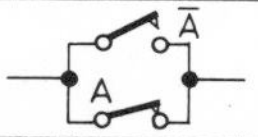

Figure 8.12

Take open to imply unoperated and closed to imply operated

E

TESTING FOR LOGICAL EQUIVALENCE

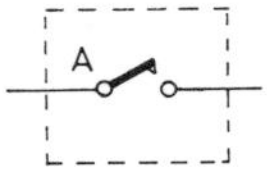

Figure 8.13(a)

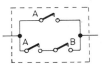

Figure 8.13(b)

Suppose we have two boxes. One contains the switching circuit shown in *Figure 8.13(a)* and the other the circuit shown at (*b*). The logical equation for circuit (*a*) should be no problem for you; it is

$$A = F$$

For circuit (*b*) you should be able to deduce that

$$A \lor (A.B) = F$$

As usual, the F simply signifies that we get an output signal when the switches are operated in the manner indicated by the equations. If the two switches marked A seem confusing, remember they are ganged together and so operate together. Now since either equation represents the same circuit condition, we should be able to say that

$$A \lor (A.B) = A$$

Clearly, this statement is true: if switch A is operated, the circuit is completed. The presence of switch B is irrelevant. So, too, is switch A in series with B. Only the top switch A is strictly necessary, hence the circuit at (*b*) is exactly equivalent to the simple circuit at (*a*), and so the latter can replace it, thereby saving two switches in the process.

The equivalence of two logical equations is a matter of great importance in the design of computers, since the ability to reduce a complicated circuit to a simpler one doing exactly same job, enables the designer to use the minimum number of circuit elements (say integrated circuits) to achieve a certain result. Can we prove the logical equivalence of two equations without recourse to circuit diagrams? The answer is yes, and there are several ways of doing it. Only one method will concern us at this stage and this is the method of proof by the use of truth tables.

A truth table is constructed for each of the expressions we are comparing for equivalence (or otherwise). If the two expressions have the same truth value (0 or 1) for each case in the truth table, then the expressions are equivalent. If at any point the truth values differ, then the expressions are not equivalent. The method is best illustrated by worked examples, so follow the next examples carefully.

Example (9). Prove, using truth tables, that $A \lor (A.B) = A$.

This is the case we previously looked at in terms of switching circuits. To prove the statement, we draw up truth tables as follows:

A	*B*	*A.B*	*A v (A.B)*
0	0	0	0
0	1	0	0
1	0	0	1
1	1	1	1

The first two columns, as usual, represent all possible arrangements of the quantities A and B. The third column is the logical AND function A.B. The fourth column is constructed in accordance with the logical OR function. We compare the A column values with the A.B column values: a 1 is placed in the fourth column when either the A column *or* the A.B. column (or both) have the value 1, and a 0 is placed in the column when the value of both the A and the A.B columns is 0.

Comparing the fourth column, i.e. A v (A.B) with the first column, A, they are seen to be identical, hence the statement A v (A.B) = A is shown to be true.

Example (10). Prove that A v $\overline{A}$.B = A v B, and illustrate the equivalence in terms of switching circuits.

As before, we draw up a truth table for both expressions and compare them.

A	B	$\overline{A}$	$\overline{A}.B$	$A \vee \overline{A}.B$	$A \vee B$
0	0	1	0	0	0
0	1	1	1	1	1
1	0	0	0	1	1
1	1	0	0	1	1

The third column ($\overline{A}$) is the negation of the first column (A). The fourth column is the logical AND function for $\overline{A}$.B and has the value 1 only when both $\overline{A}$ and B are simultaneously 1, i.e. the second row condition. The fifth column is the logical OR function and has the value 1 when either the A column or the $\overline{A}$.B column (or both) have the value 1. The last column is the OR function A v B.

Comparison of the fifth column with the sixth shows them to be identical, hence the statement A v $\overline{A}$B = A v B is true.

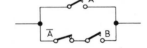

Figure 8.14(a)

Figure 8.14(a) shows the circuit representation of A v AB, and (*b*) shows the representation of A v B. These should be identical in circuit function. In (*a*) the circuit is completed if A is closed (note that $\overline{A}$ then opens) or if A is left open (so that $\overline{A}$ remains closed) and B is closed, i.e. A v $\overline{A}$.B is satisfied. So all that is *necessary* for circuit completion is the closure of either A or B; switch $\overline{A}$ is redundant to the operation. Circuit (*b*) representing A v B is then identical to circuit (*a*).

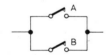

Figure 8.14(b)

PROBLEMS FOR SECTION 8

Group 1

(11) What logical functions are represented by the following truth tables:

A	B	F		A	B	F		A	B	F
0	0	0		0	0	0		0	0	1
0	1	1		0	1	0		0	1	0
1	0	1		1	0	0		1	0	0
1	1	1		1	1	1		1	1	1

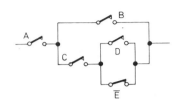

Figure 8.15

(12) Draw circuit diagrams and truth tables to represent the following logical expressions:
   (a) A(B v C)
   (b) (A v B).(A v C)
   (c) A($\bar{A}$ v B)

(13) A circuit which is OR with positive logic will be . . . . . . with negative logic.

(14) Write down the logical expression for the circuit shown in *Figure 8.15*.

(15) Use truth tables to verify the following statements:
   (a) A v B.C = (A v B)(A v C)
   (b) A(B v C) = A.B v A.C
   (c) (A v B)(A.B) = A.B

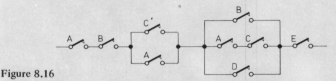

Figure 8.16

Group 2

(16) Write down the logical expression representing the circuit shown in *Figure 8.16*. Verify that your solution can be represented by the simple form F = A.B.E.

(17) What logical expression does the following truth table represent?

A	B	C	F
0	0	0	0
0	0	1	1
0	1	0	1
0	1	1	0
1	0	0	0
1	0	1	1
1	1	0	1
1	1	1	0

Draw the circuit interpretation of the expression.

(18) The expressions 0.0 = 0 and 1.1 = 1 are illustrated respectively at (a) and (b) in *Figure 8.17*. Using these as a guide, draw the circuit interpretations of
   (a) 0 v 0 = 0   (b) 1 v 1 = 1   (c) 1 v 0 = 1
   (d) A v 1 = 1   (e) A v 0 = A   (f) A.0 = 0
   (g) A.1 = A

(19) Verify the following statements:
   (a) A($\bar{A}$ v B) = A.B
   (b) (A v $\bar{B}$)(A v C) = A v $\bar{B}$.C
   (c) $\overline{A v B}$ = $\overline{A}.\overline{B}$
   (d) $\overline{A v B}$ = $\overline{A}.\overline{B}$

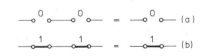

Figure 8.17

These last two expressions are known as De Morgan's Rules and you will meet them again in more advanced work. You should make a note that $\overline{A.B}$ means 'not (A and B)'. It is not the same as $\overline{A}.\overline{B}$ which means 'not A *and* not B'.

9 Electronic gate elements

Aims: At the end of this Unit section you should be able to:
Recognise the symbols for AND, OR and NOT logic gate elements.
Understand the action of the basic electronic gate.
Explain the operation of three-input diode AND and OR logic gates.
Explain the operation of a transistor NOT gate.
Draw the circuit representations of simple logical expressions.
Derive the combinational circuits for NAND, NOR and Exclusive OR gates.

ELECTRONIC GATES

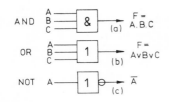

Figure 9.1

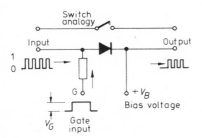

Figure 9.2

So far we have dealt only with logical relationships and their interpretation in the form of simple switching circuits. In order to use these relationships in practical applications it is necessary to design a system of electronic gate elements which will enable the desired relationship between input and output signal levels to be achieved by purely electronic means. The three basic gates of interest to us at this point are those corresponding to the three logical functions dealt with in the previous Unit section, i.e. the AND, OR and NOT gates. The symbols representing these gates are illustrated in *Figure 9.1*. We have assumed that there are three inputs to the AND and OR gates, though any number may be involved in practice, and each has one output, designated F. The NOT gate is simply an inverter and has one output which is the *negation* of the single input.

Each of the inputs to these gates will consist of electrical signals which may represent one or other of two possible states. For example, two voltage levels may be involved, zero voltage corresponding to 0 in the logical algebra and, say, + 5 V corresponding to logical 1. This would be an example of positive logic. Any two dissimilar voltage levels may be used as input signal representations of logic 0 and 1.

In this Unit section we shall cover these basic circuits, together with a few important combinations of them, which will perform the required logical operations. We shall assume that the diodes used in these circuits are ideal in having zero forward resistance and infinite reverse resistance; this assumption will in no way invalidate the explanations of the circuit functions.

A FUNDAMENTAL DIODE GATE

A gate, as its name implies, is a switch that is either open or closed. The most fundamental gate is a simple switch which connects input to output as shown in *Figure 9.2*. Although such a mechanically operated device would not be used in any practical computer gate applications (apart perhaps from switching the power supply on and off!), its action does nevertheless represent the action of all electronic gate circuits, however sophisticated or complex.

A simple electronic equivalent to the switch of *Figure 9.2* is shown immediately below it. A semiconductor diode is connected in series with the input and output terminals of a circuit. At the input, a series of pulses represents the logical states 0 and 1 in regular succession. A positive d.c. bias voltage V_B is applied to the cathode of the diode so that, with no signal present at the gate input terminal G, the diode is switched off. As a result, no signal passes from input to output terminals via the diode. Now let a square wave, whose amplitude V_G is greater than the d.c. bias voltage V_B, be applied to the gate terminal. V_G makes the anode of the diode more positive than its cathode and the diode switches on. For the duration of the gate input pulse, therefore, signals can pass from input to output via the diode. As shown in the diagram, only a few of the input pulse trains are allowed to pass through.

Although this system represents a true electronic gate, it is limited in its action to a simple stop-and-go function, and as it is depicted here it has no particular application to the three basic logic gates shown in *Figure 9.1*. But it provides us with a starting point.

THE DIODE AND GATE

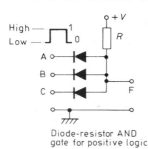

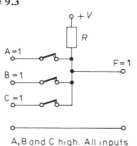

Diode-resistor AND gate for positive logic

Figure 9.3

The logical AND circuit receives a number of input signals but does not deliver an output unless all the inputs are present. If therefore the input signals are designated A, B and C, there is an output only if A and B and C are simultaneously present, that is, F = A.B.C, as the first diagram of *Figure 9.1* shows. For this reason, the AND gate is often referred to as a *coincidence gate*.

We now look at the case of a diode AND gate. *Figure 9.3* illustrates three inputs, although the following argument will apply equally to the case of four or more inputs. The magnitude of the positive anode supply voltage V is usually made several times greater than the positive level of the gate input pulses. The operation of the gate is then relatively easy to follow through.

Suppose all input signals are simultaneously high; then *all* the diodes conduct because of the more positive anode voltage, and the output is connected to the high level inputs directly through the diodes. Hence the output is high. The switch analogy of this case is shown in *Figure 9.4(a)*. Assume now that any one of the inputs, A, for example, goes low. The cathode of diode A is then low but the anode is high, hence the diode conducts and connects the output to the low level A input terminal. This has the effect of bringing the anodes of diodes B and C also to a low level since all the anodes are connected together. Hence the presence of high level conditions at the *cathodes* of B and C in conjunction with the low level *anodes* causes these two diodes to switch off, and no signals from inputs B and C can reach the output. The output is correspondingly low, as the switch analogy of *Figure 9.4(b)* shows. By exactly the same reasoning (which you should go through in detail for yourself), the output will be low whenever any two of the inputs are low and the third is high or all three are low. Only the *simultaneous* presence of high input levels at all three input terminals produces a high output, hence the circuit performs as a logical AND gate for *positive logic* inputs. For this reason, this particular form of circuit is known as a *positive AND gate*.

Input pulses are not always of the same duration, so it is possible for the AND gate to act as a detector of coincidence among several inputs. A possible train of positive input pulses at points A, B and C is shown in *Figure 9.5*. Only when terminals A, B and C are simultaneously high will there be an output F. From the diagram, this state of affairs occurs only during the time interval t_1 to t_2.

A, B and C high. All inputs are connected to the output, hence the output is high

Figure 9.4(a)

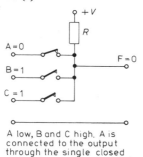

A low, B and C high. A is connected to the output through the single closed switch hence the output is low

Figure 9.4(b)

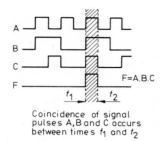

Coincidence of signal
pulses A,B and C occurs
between times t_1 and t_2

Figure 9.5

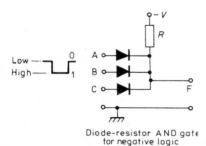

Diode-resistor AND gate
for negative logic

Figure 9.6

Suppose we require an AND gate which will operate from negative logic. The design of such a gate is now remarkably simple: we simply reverse the diodes and apply a negative supply voltage, so making a *negative AND gate*. *Figure 9.6* shows the modified circuit and you should compare this, and the nature of its input pulses, with the positive AND gate of *Figure 9.3*. Recall that in negative logic, the low voltage level becomes logic 1 and the high voltage level becomes logic 0. For example, the input pulses may vary between −5 V (logic 1) and zero volts (logic 0). Go back to *Figure 9.6*. It is usual to make the negative supply several times the value of the most negative excursion of the input pulses, so for −5 V, say, representing logic 1 as above, V might be made −15 V. Suppose now that one of the inputs, A, for example, goes low, the diode will conduct and place all the cathodes at zero voltage. Diodes B and C then have −5 V (high) on their anodes and zero volts on their cathodes, so they switch off; hence the output is low. The output is only high (that is, at −5 V) if all three inputs are simultaneously at −5 V. Follow the operation through for yourself. Thus the circuit is a negative AND gate because the 'high' input condition this time is more negative than the 'low', i.e. negative logic.

> (1) Complete the following statements:
> (a) The AND gate is sometimes referred to as a . . . . . gate.
> (b) An AND gate behaves like a . . . . connected switch circuit.
> (c) When only signal C is present at the input of a gate representing the expression F = A.B.C, the output signal is . . . . . .
> (d) A diode AND gate provides zero (or low) volts at its output when one or more of its diodes are . . . . biased.

THE DIODE OR GATE

An OR gate, symbolised in *Figure 9.1(b)*, provides an output if any one of its inputs are present. If therefore the input signals are designated A, B and C, there is an output if A or B or C is present, i.e. F = A v B v C. At this point we must distinguish between two different kinds of OR gate. Consider a two-input OR gate; if an output is obtained if A = 1 or B = 1 or if both are 1, the gate is known as the *inclusive OR*. If, however, an output is obtained only if A = 1 or B = 1, but not if both equal 1, the gate is known as the *exclusive OR*. Our previous analogy of an OR gate to switches connected in parallel was the inclusive case, and the OR circuit truth table (*Table 8.2*), to which you should refer back, illustrates the inclusive case. The symbol for the exclusive OR gate is similar to that for the inclusive OR shown in *Figure 9.1*, but the internal 1 is replaced by =1. We shall return to the exclusive OR case a little later on.

Look at the diode logic circuit of *Figure 9.7*. The diode cathodes are returned to a negative voltage point and the input pulses conform to positive logic convention, high = 1, low = 0. This circuit will perform the OR function in which any single high input will produce a high output. When all the inputs are low (0) all diodes conduct, the cathodes being negative with respect to the anodes. The output is then connected directly to the input and so the output is low. This condition corresponds to the first row of the truth table in the figure. Suppose now that any input, say input C, goes high (1). Diode C will conduct and the output will be high; diodes A and B then have high cathodes but low anodes

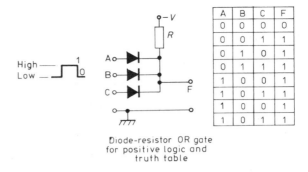

A	B	C	F
0	0	0	0
0	0	1	1
0	1	0	1
0	1	1	1
1	0	0	1
1	0	1	1
1	0	0	1
1	0	1	1

Diode-resistor OR gate
for positive logic and
truth table

Figure 9.7

and consequently switch off. This condition clearly applies for any other input, or combinations of the inputs, being high, hence the truth table can be completed as shown.

What kind of table is it? There is an output 1 whenever A or B or C or any combination of them, equals 1, which is the truth table for the logical OR function. The circuit therefore performs as a logical OR gate for positive logic inputs. You should now work out for yourself, as in the case of the AND gates already discussed, that reversal of the diodes and the applied voltage V results in a circuit representing a *negative OR gate.*

(2) Does the circuit of *Figure 9.7* represent an inclusive or an exclusive OR gate?

(3) Sketch a circuit of a negative OR gate having three inputs. Use *Figure 9.7* and the last note in the text as a guide line. Compare your sketch with *Figure 9.3*. What do you notice about them?

(4) *Figure 9.8* shows a train of input pulses which are applied in turn to three-input (i) positive AND gate, (ii) positive inclusive OR gate, (iii) positive exclusive OR gate. The time scale indicates milliseconds of duration. Between what times are there outputs from (a) the AND gate (b) the OR, (c) the exclusive OR gate?

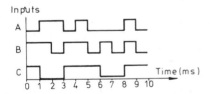

Figure 9.8

If, as you should have discovered in solving Problem (2), we compare the positive AND gate with the negative OR gate, we find they are identical in circuit arrangement and in applied bias voltage. In exactly the same way, a comparison of a positive OR gate with a negative AND gate will show them to be identical; *Figure 9.6* is identical with *Figure 9.7*. So any group of diodes can act either as AND or OR gates, depending upon the polarity (logic convention) of the input signals and the purpose for which it is required. Positive AND is the same as negative OR except that the output is high only if *all* inputs are high, while for negative OR the output is low if *any* of the inputs are low. Conversely, negative AND is the same as positive OR except that the output is low only if *all* inputs are low, while for positive OR the output is high only if *any* of the inputs are high.

Unless the contrary is indicated, we shall assume that all text references to AND and OR gates refer to positive circuits so that all input signals conform to positive logic.

(5) A diode OR gate provides a positive voltage at its output when one or more diodes are . . . . biased.

(6) A gate has two inputs A and B and one output F. The table shows the possible states of input and output signals. What type of gate is this?

A	B	F
0	0	0
0	1	1
1	0	1
1	1	0

THE NOT GATE

The logical NOT function (or *negation*), symbolised in *Figure 9.1(c)*, has one input and one output connection, the output being the inversion of the input. For an input A, the output is $\overline{A}$ (not-A), and vice versa. An inversion cannot be performed by diode and resistor combinations and this is one of the major disadvantages of electronic gates made up from diode and resistor elements only. However, as we have seen in an earlier section, a transistor connected in common-emitter mode is an inverter of signal polarity, so the circuit of *Figure 9.9* will serve as a basic NOT gate. For illustration we are taking the input levels to be either zero (0) or $+V_{CC}$ (1), though in practice such levels would be represented by signal pulses applied to the base of the transistor. When the input is at logic level 0, the base current is zero and the transistor is switched off. Ignoring leakage current, the collector current is then zero and the collector potential is at $+V_{CC}$, logic level 1. When the input is at logic level 1 $(+V_{CC})$ sufficient base current flows for the transistor to be saturated and the collector potential falls (almost) to zero, logic level 0. In either of these cases, the output logic level is the reverse or negation of the input level, hence the circuit acts as a negator or NOT gate. Typical input and output waveforms are shown at the side of *Figure 9.9*.

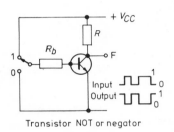

Transistor NOT or negator

Figure 9.9

CIRCUIT REPRESENTATION OF LOGICAL EXPRESSIONS

Up to this point, we have explained logic gates in the form of single elements. Using the three basic elements of AND, OR and NOT functions, it is possible to derive arrangements and combinations which represent a great number of logical expressions.

Consider a two-input AND gate. *Figure 9.10* shows four possible output expressions for the logical AND. By the inclusion of the NOT gate in three of the combinations, outputs representing the logical expressions A.B, $\overline{A}$.B, A.$\overline{B}$ and $\overline{A.B}$ are obtained. Make sure you understand how each of these outputs results. You can do this best by considering the 'intermediate' input states shown arrowed; for example, in case (b), input A is inverted to $\overline{A}$ and this together with B forms the input to the AND gate. The final output is then $\overline{A}$.B.

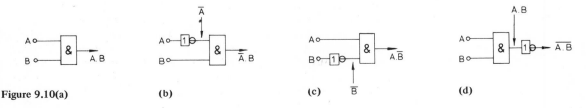

Figure 9.10(a)   (b)   (c)   (d)

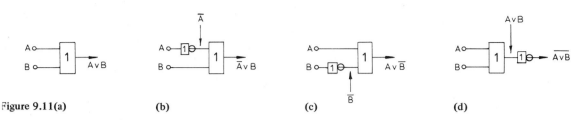

Figure 9.11(a) **(b)** **(c)** **(d)**

In a similar manner, *Figure 9.11* shows four possible output expressions for the logical OR. By combinations of this kind, a great variety of expressions and conditions essential to computer design in particular can be evolved. Some of these are more important than others, and we shall discuss two of these in a little more detail.

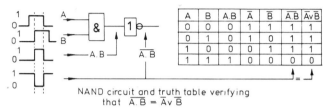

A	B	A.B	$\overline{A}$	$\overline{B}$	$\overline{A.B}$	$\overline{A}v\overline{B}$
0	0	0	1	1	1	1
0	1	0	1	0	1	1
1	0	0	0	1	1	1
1	1	1	0	0	0	0

NAND circuit and truth table verifying
that $\overline{A.B} = \overline{A}v\overline{B}$

Figure 9.12

1. *NOT AND circuit.* This circuit, known as the *NAND* element, is shown in *Figure 9.10(d)*, and illustrated in more detail in *Figure 9.12*. When A.B is applied to the input of the NOT gate, the output is $\overline{A.B}$. Notice the negation bar is drawn across both A and B. The $\overline{A.B}$ means the inverter negates A to $\overline{A}$, AND to OR, and inverts B to $\overline{B}$. Therefore, as a glance at the accompanying truth table will verify,

$$\overline{A.B} = \overline{A}v\overline{B}$$

You may recognise this expression as one of De Morgan's rules which you verified in Problem (18) of the previous section. The NAND gate is a very important element in logical circuit design.

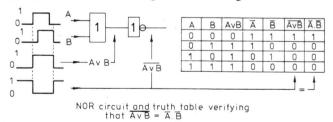

A	B	AvB	$\overline{A}$	$\overline{B}$	$\overline{AvB}$	$\overline{A}.\overline{B}$
0	0	0	1	1	1	1
0	1	1	1	0	0	0
1	0	1	0	1	0	0
1	1	1	0	0	0	0

NOR circuit and truth table verifying
that $\overline{AvB} = \overline{A}.\overline{B}$

Figure 9.13

2. *NOT OR circuit.* This circuit, known as the *NOR* element, is shown in *Figure 9.11(d)*, and illustrated in more detail in *Figure 9.13*. Like the NAND circuit, this has several inputs and one output. When there is a signal on one of the inputs or on any combination of the inputs there is a NOT signal at the output. In symbols, $\overline{A v B}$ (notice again that the negation bar implies that NOT applies to the whole term) means the inverter negates A to $\overline{A}$, the OR to AND, and B to $\overline{B}$. Again referring to the truth table, we see

$$\overline{A v B} = \overline{A}.\overline{B}$$

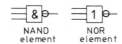

NAND   NOR
element   element

Figure 9.14

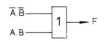

Figure 9.15(a)

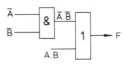

Figure 9.15(b)

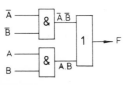

Figure 9.15(c)

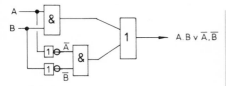

Figure 9.15(d)

This is the second of De Morgan's rules. Like the NAND gate, the NOR gate is an important element in logical design.

The symbols for the NAND and NOR gates are shown in *Figure 9.14*.

Some worked examples now follow. Go through these carefully and then try the self-assessment problems which come after.

Example (7). Devise a circuit whose output represents the function $F = A.B \lor \overline{A}.\overline{B}$, given two inputs A and B, and using only AND, OR and NOT elements.

We notice that the terms $A.B$, $\overline{A}.\overline{B}$ are linked by the OR symbol; these two terms will therefore be the output of an OR gate which has inputs $A.B$, $\overline{A}.\overline{B}$. This condition is illustrated in *Figure 9.15(a)*. The $\overline{A}.\overline{B}$ term has to be the ouput of an AND gate having inputs $\overline{A}$ and $\overline{B}$; this brings us to diagram (*b*). Similarly, the A.B input term will be the output of another AND gate for which the inputs are respectively A and B; diagram (*c*). To complete the picture, we can produce $\overline{A}$ and $\overline{B}$ signals by inversion of the A and B primary inputs, and the final circuit then appears at (*d*).

It is important to bear in mind that the solution given is not necessarily the simplest or most economical way of achieving the required expression.

Example (8). We have already said that the exclusive OR gate gives an output only if A = 1 or B = 1, but not if both equal 1. Devise a circuit made up from AND, OR and NOT elements that will perform the function of exclusive OR.

We have to think about the outputs we expect from the exclusive OR when the inputs available are A and B. In the inclusive OR we have an output when A = 1, B = 1 or both equal 1. From the truth table, this output is fully represented by the expression

$$F = \overline{A}.B \lor A.\overline{B} \lor AB$$

Inclusive OR				Exclusive OR		
A	*B*	*F*		*A*	*B*	*F*
0	0	0		0	0	0
0	1	1	$\longrightarrow \overline{A}.B$	0	1	1	$\longrightarrow \overline{A}.B$
1	0	1	$\longrightarrow A.\overline{B}$	1	0	1	$\longrightarrow A.\overline{B}$
1	1	1	$\longrightarrow A.B$	1	1	0	

This may appear to be different from the OR circuit expression $F = A \lor B$ we have always used up to this point, but it is necessary to express the function in this extended form in order to put our solution into circuit element form. It can be proved by simple logical algebra (you might care to try it) that $A.\overline{B} \lor \overline{A}.B \lor A.B$ is exactly the same as $A \lor B$.

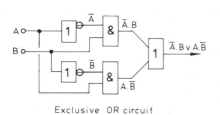

Exclusive OR circuit

Figure 9.16

From the second truth table, the exclusive OR expression is

$$F = A.\overline{B} \vee \overline{A}.B$$

the A.B term which was present in the inclusive OR case being excluded by definition. This is the expression we require to set up the necessary gate element combination circuit which will represent the exclusive OR function.

Figure 9.16 shows the required combination. It is derived by a process exactly similar to that used in the previous example. A.$\overline{B}$, $\overline{A}$.B are connected by the OR symbol, hence they are the outputs of an OR gate having the separate inputs A.$\overline{B}$ and $\overline{A}$.B. These two terms are in turn connected by the AND symbol, so each is the ouput of AND gates having respective twin inputs A and $\overline{B}$, $\overline{A}$ and B. The negated signals are derived in turn from two NOT gates wired into the primary A and B input lines as shown. Hence the complete exclusive OR circuit is made up from one OR element, two NOT and two AND elements. The OR element here is, of course, an inclusive case.

A Note on Logic   This is as far as it is necessary for you to study logical expressions and related circuits at this stage of the programme. The contents of the last two Unit sections may well have been unfamiliar and possibly even bizarre to you, but they form the basic methods and circuitry of the electronic logic systems used in the design of calculators, computers and industrial control systems, and consequently are of vital and increasing importance in electronic study programmes. Work through the Unit sections again if necessary, and you should then have no difficulty in answering the following problems.

PROBLEMS FOR SECTION 9

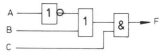

Figure 9.17(a)

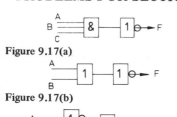

Figure 9.17(b)

Figure 9.17(c)

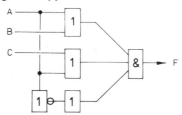

Figure 9.17(d)

(9) Complete the following:
    (a) When logical 0 is at the input of a NOT element, the output signal is logical . . . .
    (b) The output A v B is provided by a(an) . . . . . gate.
    (c) A NOR gate with a single input is equivalent to a . . . . . . gate.
    (d) An exclusive OR gate consists of . . . . NOT, ... OR and . . . . AND elements.
    (e) A NOR circuit includes both . . . . and . . . . elements.
    (f) A positive logic AND gate is equivalent to a . . . . . logic . . . . gate.
    (g) A NOT AND gate is called a . . . . . . gate.
(10) Deduce the logical expression for the output F of each of the circuits shown in *Figure 9.17*.
(11) Construct a truth table for a NOR circuit having two inputs A and B.
(12) In the circuit of *Figure 9.18* the input signal levels are either 0 V or +10 V. Answer the following:
    (a) Under what condition(s) will the potential at X be +10 V?
    (b) What then will be the potential at Y?
    (c) What logic function does the circuit perform?

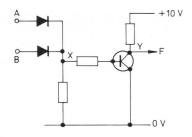

Figure 9.18

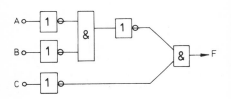

Figure 9.19

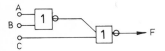

Figure 9.20

(13) Use truth tables to verify the following equations:
(a) $\overline{A} \vee \overline{B} \vee \overline{C} = \overline{A.B.C}$ (b) $A \vee \overline{A}.B = A \vee B$
(c) $A.(\overline{A} \vee B) = A.B$ (d) $A.B \vee A.C = A.(B \vee C)$
(e) $A\overline{B} \vee \overline{A}B \vee AB = A \vee B$ (f) $\overline{A} \vee \overline{C}.(A \vee B) \vee C = 1$

(14) Two logic elements are connected together as shown in *Figure 9.19*. What single logical operation does the circuit perform?

(15) The truth table following represents the operation of a logic circuit. What is the logical expression for the output of the circuit?

A	B	F
0	0	1
0	1	0
1	0	0
1	1	1

(16) Write down the logical equations representing the output of the circuits shown in *Figure 9.20*. Use truth tables to prove that both circuits are identical as far as function is concerned. What fact of importance do you think this example illustrates?

(17) A machine operator controls red and green indicator lights by four switches, A, B, C and D. The sequence of operation is as follows:

(i) Red light is ON when switch A is ON and switch B is OFF or switch C is ON.

(ii) Green light is ON when switches A and B are ON and switches C and D are off.

Write down logical expressions representing the conditions (i) and (ii) and draw logical circuits depicting these expressions.

(18) Complete the following:

(a) If one of six inputs to an OR gate is logical 1, the output is logical . . . .

(b) A diode OR gate provides a positive (high) voltage at its output when one or more diodes are . . . . biased.

(c) The positive AND and the negative OR function is expressed in logical algebra by $F = $ . . . . . .

(d) If input A to a two-input NAND gate is logical 1, input B must be logical . . . . . for the equation $F = A \vee \overline{B}$ to be satisfied.

(e) A circuit which is NAND with positive logic will be . . . . with negative logic.

(f) The circuit represented by the expression $\overline{F} = A \vee B$ is

. . . . . .

(19) A two-input AND gate can be made up from three NOT elements. Sketch a suitable arrangement. How could this arrangement be made into a NAND circuit by the addition of one or more NOT elements?

Solutions to problems

UNIT SECTION 1

(1) 29

(2) 3

(3) (a) No, a coated wire may be directly heated. (b) No, emission is the same for the same temperatures. (c) No emission still takes place but electrons return from the cloud and so maintain an equilibrium state.

(4) (a) Neutrons, protons, (b) 1840, (c) valence, (d) hydrogen, (e) cathode material, temperature, (f) holes, (g) conductivity, resistance.

(5) (a) True, (b) true, (c) false.

(6) Your table should look like this:

	Protons	K	L	M
Alum.	13	2	8	3
Silic.	14	2	8	4
Phos.	15	2	8	5
Chlor.	17	2	8	7

(7) There are three valence electrons, therefore gallium impurity is p-type.

(8) Germanium; four; four; four.

UNIT SECTION 2

(1) No.

(2) Slightly greater than.

(3) (i) Increases slightly. (ii) Rapidly increases, but is small.

(4) 320 μA.

(5) Yes.

(8) (a) Cathode, (b) space-charge limited (linear), (c) forward, reverse, (d) temperature, (e) same, as.

(9)(a) False, it has only one.

(b) True.

(c) False; all external wires have electron carriers.

(d) True, assuming the temperatures are the same.

(e) True.

(11) About 1.6 mA.

(13) Infinite reverse resistance, zero forward resistance. The curve would simply follow the coordinate axes defining the second quadrant.

(14) Cathode.

(15) No. Thermionic diodes operate at temperatures far above ambient, so changes in ambient have no effect. Also, there are no minority carriers and so no reverse leakage current in the thermionic diode.

(17) (i) 3.0 A in 2 Ω, 1.5 A in 4 Ω; (ii) 1.5 A in 4 Ω, 1.0 A in 6 Ω.

(18) As a capacitor; this application will be covered in the next section.

(19) As a constant voltage source; this is also covered in section 3.

(20) (i) 11.5 mA. (ii) 70.75 V.

(22) As heat at the anode.

UNIT SECTION 3

(1) No, the stated 250 V will be r.m.s. and this has a peak value 354 V.

(2) The peak output is 495 V on each secondary; hence the p.i.v. on the diodes will be twice this, or about 1 kV.

(3) The output voltage will be reduced by the voltage drop across R_f.

$$\text{Average } I = \frac{0.318 \, \hat{V}}{R_L + R_f} \; ; \qquad \text{r.m.s. } I = \frac{0.5 \, \hat{V}}{R_L + R_f}$$

(8) (a) Zero, infinite, (b) zero, (c) space-charge, (d) $\sqrt{(2 \, V)}/\pi$, (e) increases, reduces, (f) twice.

(9) 28.3 V.

(10) (a) 0.177 A, (b) 30 W, (c) 0.354 A.

(11) (a) 0.155 A, (b) 31 V, (c) 0.775 A.

(12) (a) 2.44 V, (b) 100 V.

(13) (a) Output voltage would be halved; (b) rectification would cease and the output would be as shown in *Figure A.1*.

(14) (a) 35.4, (b) 1.25 A.

(15) 5.0.

(17) 400 Ω.

(18) 45.5 Ω, 0.35 W.

(19) 44 V maximum to 24.2 V minimum.

(20) 725 Ω.

(21) 24.5 pF.

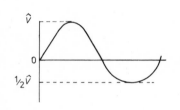

Figure A.1

UNIT SECTION 4

(1) *p-n-p*.

(2) Common-emitter.

(3) Positive.

(4) 0.1 mA.

(5) (i) 0.96, (ii) 24.

(6) I_E/I_B.

(7) 0.99.

(8) 65.7.

(9) 30–40 Ω; 7000–8000 Ω.

(10) If V_{CB} is reduced to zero, the collector is still able to gather electrons from the base because of the junction p.d. developed across the depletion layer. refer back to page 11.

(11) About 100.

(12) (a) Forward, reverse, (b) electron, (c) negative, (d) away from, (e) common-base, (f) smaller, (g) I_E.

(13) (a) 49, (b) 39, (c) 32.3, (d) 24.

(14) (a) 0.98, (b)).987, (c) 0.991, (d) 0.997.

(15) 0.993, 149.

(16) (a) (i) False, it depends only upon V_{BE}. (ii) False, it depends only upon I_E. (iii) True, for V_{CB} above about 0.2 V.

(b) False, a leakage current flows from collector to emitter.
(c) False; if they were the collector would not collect them.
(d) False.
(17) 6 kΩ.
(18) 200 kΩ.
(19) 1230 Ω.
(20) 13 Ω.
(21) About 1 kΩ.

UNIT SECTION 5

(1) No fundamental reason at all, but a very large V_{CC} would be necessary to allow for the very large voltage drop across R_L. For more normal V_{CC} supplies, the resistor of large value would leave very little working voltage at the collector.
(2) No, input current is in phase with the output current.
(4) Because the equation of the load line is $V_{CC} = V_{CE} + I_C R_L$ and this is the equation of a linear graph.
(5) The ratio of 5.6 mA to 150 μA; about 37 times.
(6) The ratio of 0.15 V input to 8.25 V output; about 55 times.
(7) 0.972.
(8) 0.714 mA.
(9) 180 kΩ.
(10) 2 V.
(13) (a) False, (b) false, V_{BE} decreases, (c) false, it is 10×10 = 100, (d) true (strictly for germanium devices), (e) true, (f) false. (When R_L = 0 the signal gain is zero.)
(14) (a) 45 μA, (b) 40, (c) 4.8 V peak-to-peak.
(15) $A_v = 1250$, $A_p = 125\,000$.
(16) (a) 5 kΩ, (b) 6.5 mA.
(17) (a) 5.1 V, (b) 1.2 kΩ.
(18) $A_v = 80$, $A_i = 33$, $A_p = 2640$.
(19) $R_L = 500$ Ω, $R_B = 110$ kΩ.
(20) $R_L = 1.2$ kΩ; $R_E = 390$ Ω; $R_1 = 8.6$ kΩ; $R_2 = 2.5$ kΩ.
(21) 11.2 mW, 18.8 mW.

UNIT SECTION 6

(1) Amplification and positive feedback.
(2) Relaxation.
(3) Current leads the voltage by 90°.
(4) 5.033 kHz.
(5) (a) Frequency, (b) amplitude, (c) non-sinusoidal, (d) common-emitter, positive, (e) halved, (f) lowest — approximately zero, (g) zero.
(6) 1592 kHz to 712 kHz.
(7) At resonance, *supply* voltage is in phase with *supply* current. The capacitor current which is 90° out of phase with the voltage within the oscillatory circuit only affects the supply current.
(8) 0.25 s.
(9) 1.2 mV; 25.
(10) Yes. The transformer can be connected to provide zero phase shift itself; the overall phase shift round the loop will then be zero, so oscillation is possible.

UNIT SECTION 7

(1) Horizontally.

(2) Give a bit of thought to *Figure 7.8* and this should answer the question.

(3) 0.36 mm/V or 2.78 V/mm.

(5) Yes. Sensitivity will increase as the plate separation is reduced, and conversely.

(6) (a) Velocity, density, (b) afterglow, (c) down, (d) electric, (e) vertically, (f) V/mm or mm/V.

(7) About 43 V/cm.

(8) The sensitivity will be reduced to two-thirds of its original value, i.e. to 4.5 V/mm.

(9) Six. The period of one cycle of the wave is 2 ms.

(10) 2.5 ms.

(11) 71 V; 800 Hz.

UNIT SECTION 8

(3) A v B v C is represented by three parallel connected switches. The required truth table follows:

A	B	C	F
0	0	0	0
0	0	1	1
0	1	0	1
0	1	1	1
1	0	0	1
1	0	1	1
1	1	0	1
1	1	1	1

(4) A v (B.C) = F.

(5) $2^4 = 16$; A(B v C) v D = F

(8) The circuits are shown in *Figure A.2*.

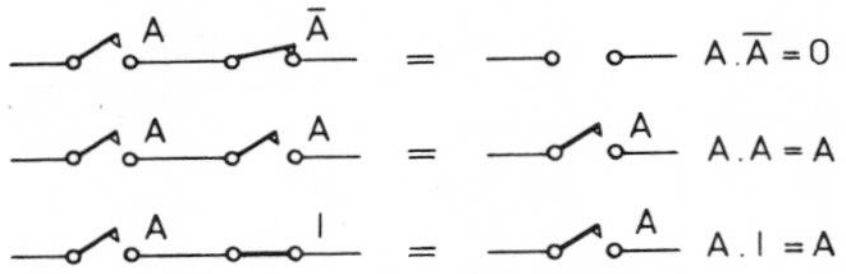

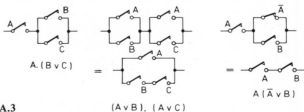

Figure A.2

(11) A v B = F; A.B = F; A.B v $\overline{A}.\overline{B}$ = F.

(12) The circuits are shown in *Figure A.3*.

Figure A.3   (A v B) . (A v C)

(13) AND.

(14) A[B v C(D v $\overline{E}$)].

(16) A.B(C v A).(B v A.C v D).E.

(17) B.$\overline{C}$ v $\overline{B}$.C.

(18) The circuits are shown in *Figure A.4*.

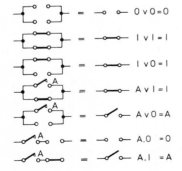

Figure A.4

UNIT SECTION 9

(1) (a) coincidence, (b) series, (c) logical 0, (d) forward.

(2) Inclusive OR.

(4) (a) 4–5 ms, 8–9 ms, (b) at all times except 7–8 ms, (c) 2–3 ms, 6–7 ms, 9–10 ms.

(5) Forward.

(6) Exclusive OR.

(9) (a) 1, (b) OR, (c) NOT, (d) 2 NOT, 1 OR, 2 AND, (e) NOT OR, (f) negative, OR, (g) NAND.

(10) (a) $\overline{A}.\overline{B}.\overline{C} = F$, (b) $\overline{A} \vee \overline{B} = F$, (c) $(\overline{A} \vee B)C = F$, (d) $(A \vee B)(A \vee C)$ A.

(12) (a) An input of 10 V positive on either A or B, (b) about 0 V, (c) NOR.

(14) AND. The second NOT cancels the first NOT, i.e. NOT AND.

(15) $\overline{A}.\overline{B}. \vee A.B$.

(16) Complicated circuits can be reduced to much simpler arrangements.

(17) Red on when $A(\overline{B} \vee C)$; green on when $A.B.\overline{C}.\overline{D}$.

(18) (a) 1, (b) forward, (c) A.B, (d) O, (e) NOR, (f) NAND.

(19) The circuits are shown in *Figure A.5*.

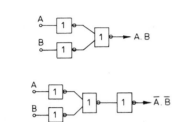

Figure A.5

Appendix

GRADIENTS

It is frequently necessary to be able to measure or calculate the *gradient* or the *slope* of a graph which represents the relationship between two variable quantities. We define the gradient of a line (see *Figure A.6*) as the tangent of the angle (θ) which the line makes with the horizontal axis. This can be found quite easily by constructing a triangle ABC as shown in the figure and applying the tangent ratio:

$$\tan \theta \;=\; \frac{BC}{AC} \;=\; \frac{\text{Change in } y}{\text{Change in } x}$$

Hence, if x changed from 2 to 6, and y correspondingly changed from 1 to 3 as the figure shows, then

$$\tan \theta \;=\; \frac{3-1}{6-2} \;=\; 0.5$$

from which, by the use of tables, $\theta = 26.6°$. However, we are not so much interested in the actual angle as in the ratio given by 0.5; this tells us the relationship existing between changes in x and the corresponding changes in y. In this example, we know that y is changing at only half the rate of x.

Obviously, if the graph is a straight line, the value obtained for the gradient would be unaffected by the size or position of the triangle ABC. The gradient of the line, in other words, is constant, a fairly self-evident fact. What happens in the case of a graph which is not a straight line, but is curved as shown in *Figure A.7(a)*? Here the gradient is not constant but changes all the time. In this case, we must define the gradient at any given point. If we choose two points on the curve, as at A and B, and complete the triangle ABC, the average gradient between A and B is given by the tangent of angle θ. Imagine now that B moves down the curve towards A; the chord AB reduces in length, and the corresponding changes in x and y also reduce. When B is extremely close to A, as in diagram (*b*), we can consider the chord AB to be coincident with the tangent PT drawn to the curve at the point in question. Hence the *gradient of the curve at this point* is given as the *gradient of the tangent PT*. As the changes in x and y are now also very small, we refer to them as dx and dy respectively, meaning 'the small change in x' and 'the small change in y' respectively. Hence

$$\text{Gradient at a point} \;=\; \frac{\text{Small change in } y}{\text{Small change in } x} \;=\; \frac{dy}{dx}$$

and this ratio is identical with the gradient of the tangent drawn to the curve at any point. It is, in fact, the *instantaneous* gradient of the curve, or the instantaneous rate of change of the variable quantities.

You will learn mathematical processes for finding the gradient of a curve at any given point when you meet up with elementary differential calculus in your mathematics course. For the present, the process of drawing a tangent to the curve at the point in question will enable you to work out what the gradient is at that point by simple triangle methods as we have just discussed.

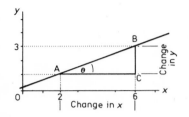

Figure A.6

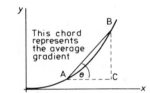

Figure A.7(a)

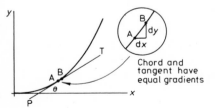

Figure A.7(b)

A checklist of books in the Newnes-Butterworths Technician Series

MATHEMATICS FOR TECHNICIANS 1

FRANK TABBERER, Chichester College of Technology

This is an introduction to mathematics for the student technician, intended especially to cover mathematics at level one in TEC courses (core unit U75/005). The presentation will create an interest in the subject particularly for those students who have previously found maths a stumbling block. There are frequent examples and exercises, with a summary and revision exercise at the end of each chapter.

CONTENTS: Manipulating numbers. Calculations. Algebra. Graphs and mappings. Statistics. Geometry. Trigonometry.

192 pages   May 1978   0 408 00326 X

MATHEMATICS FOR TECHNICIANS 2

FRANK TABBERER, Chichester College of Technology

This will cover mathematics at level two in TEC courses (units U75/012 and either U75/038 or U75/039), for those who have completed (or gained exemption from) the work in *Mathematics for Technicians 1*. It will include the alternative schemes of work allowed in the second stage of level two. The presentation and systems of examples and exercises will be similar to those in the first volume.

September 1978   0 408 00371 5

PHYSICAL SCIENCE FOR TECHNICIANS 1

R. McMULLAN, Willesden College of Technology

This is intended for students studying the Physical Science level one unit of programmes leading to TEC certificates and diplomas. The text meets the requirements of the standard TEC syllabus for physical science (unit U75/004), a core unit of courses in building, civil engineering, electrical engineering and mechanical engineering. Attention has been paid to the visual presentation of the text, which is illustrated with diagrams and examples. Important concepts and formulae are clearly highlighted as an aid to learning and revision.

CONTENTS: Introduction. Fundamentals. Force and materials. Structure of matter. Work, energy, power. Heat. Waves. Electricity. Force and motion. Forces at rest. Pressure and fluids. Chemical reactions. Light. Index.

96 pages   May 1978   0 408 00332 4

ELECTRICAL PRINCIPLES FOR TECHNICIANS 2

S. A. KNIGHT, Bedford College of Higher Education

Easy to read and in close conformity with the TEC syllabus, this book is intended primarily to cover TEC unit U75/019, Electrical Principles 2, an essential unit for both telecommunications and electronics students. The text includes examples, worked out for the reader, as well as problems for self-assessment, answers to which will be found at the end of the book. SI units are used exclusively throughout.

CONTENTS: Units and definitions. Series and parallel circuits. Electrical networks. Capacitors and capacitance. Capacitors in circuit. Magnetism and magnetisation. Electromagnetic induction. Alternating voltages and currents. Magnetic circuits. Reactance and impedance. Power and resonance. A.C. to D.C. conversion. Instruments and measurements. Alternating current measurements.

144 pages   May 1978   0 408 00325 1

ELECTRONICS FOR TECHNICIANS 2

S. A. KNIGHT, Bedford College of Higher Education

Provides an introduction to the basic theory and application of semiconductors. It covers the essential syllabus and requirements of TEC unit U76/010, Electronics 2, though some additional notes have been added for clarity. The text includes examples and self-assessment problems.

CONTENTS: Thermionic and semiconductor theory. Semiconductor and thermionic diodes. Applications of semiconductor diodes. The bipolar transistor. The transistor as amplifier. Oscillators. The cathode ray tube. Logic circuits. Electronic gate elements.

168 pages   June 1978   0 408 00324 3

BUILDING TECHNOLOGY 1 & 2

JACK BOWYER, Croydon College of Arts and Technology

These textbooks are primarily intended for the building technician taking TEC B2 construction courses. The clarity of text and illustrations should also, however, appeal to students of architecture and quantity surveying who need a good solid grounding in building construction.

BUILDING TECHNOLOGY 1

CONTENTS: The building industry. Site investigation, setting out and plant. Building elements: practice and materials. The substructure of building. The superstructure of building. Appendix: Building Standards (Scotland) Regulations 1971—75.

96 pages   March 1978   0 408 00298 0

BUILDING TECHNOLOGY 2

CONTENTS: First fixing joinery and windows. Services and drainage. Finishes and finishings. Second fixing joinery and doors. Site works, roads and pavings. Appendix: Building Standards (Scotland) Regulations 1971—75.

96 pages   May 1978   0 408 00299 9

HEATING AND HOT WATER SERVICES FOR TECHNICIANS

KEITH MOSS, City of Bath Technical College

By a system of nearly 200 worked examples, the author describes the routine design procedures for heating and hot water services in commercial and industrial buildings. Primarily intended for student HVAC technicians (TEC sector B3), it will also be useful for other students in sectors B2 and B3, and as a revision aid for experienced HVAC technicians encountering a change from Imperial to SI measurement.

CONTENTS: Heat energy transfer. Heat energy requirements of heated buildings. Heat energy losses from heated buildings. Space heating appliances. Heat energy emission. Heating and hot water service systems. The feed and expansion tank. Three-way control valves and boiler plant diagrams. Steam generation. Steam systems. Preliminary pipe sizing. Circuit balancing. Hydraulic resistance in pipes and fittings. Proportioning pipe emission. Hot and cold water supply. Circulating pumps. Steam and condense pipe sizing. Heat losses using environmental temperature. Medium and high pressure hot water heating. Index.

168 pages   July 1978   0 408 00300 6

NOTES

NOTES

NOTES